Basic Math

Page 5

1.	>	13.	>
2.	<	14.	<
3.	>	15.	<
4.	>	16.	>
5.	<	17.	>
6.	<	18.	=
7.	=	19.	<
8.	<	20.	=
9.	>	21.	>
10.	<	22.	>
11.	<	23.	<
12.	<	24.	>

Word Problem Blue Streak

Page 6

1. Thousands
2. Tens
3. Thousands
4. Hundreds
5. Thousands
6. Ten-thousands
7. Ten-thousands
8. Tens
9. Ten-thousands
10. Hundreds
11. Tens
12. Hundreds
13. Hundred-thousands
14. Millions
15. Ten-millions
16. Hundred-thousands
17. Tens
18. Hundreds
19. Thousands
20. Ten-thousands
21. Thousands
22. Ten-thousands
23. Ones
24. Thousands
25. Hundreds
26. Ones
27. Thousands
28. Ten-thousands
29. Ones
30. Millions

Page 7

1.	5,684	9.	2,690
2.	8,730	10.	33,562
3.	90,270	11.	14,074
4.	50,270	12.	20,690
5.	93,613	13.	8,715
6.	429,647	14.	573,849
7.	193,281	15.	63,286
8.	725,439	16.	292,407

Calculator 2,474

Page 8

1. 200 + 70 + 6
2. 4,000 + 100 + 80 + 5
3. 5,000 + 20 + 3
4. 10,000 + 6,000 + 300 + 80 + 3
5. 20,000 + 4,000 + 70 + 6
6. 40,000 + 9,000 + 200 + 8
7. 10,000 + 8,000 + 200 + 30 + 4
8. 200,000 + 10,000 + 3,000 + 500 + 30 + 7
9. 4,000,000 + 600,000 + 80,000 + 7,000 + 600 + 50 + 4
10. 100,000 + 20,000 + 3,000 + 200 + 10 + 8
11. 40,000 + 2,000 + 700 + 20 + 1
12. 5,000,000 + 800,000 + 10,000 + 7,000 + 200 + 90 + 5
13. 7,000,000 + 100,000 + 80,000 + 2,000 + 900 + 90 + 8
14. 50,000 + 4,000 + 200 + 80 + 1
15. 1,000,000 + 400,000 + 40,000 + 5,000 + 100 + 20 + 3
16. 500,000 + 70,000 + 800 + 20 + 1
17. 2,000 + 800 + 50 + 7
18. 70,000 + 2,000 + 600 + 90 + 5
19. 300,000 + 80,000 + 9,000 + 400 + 20 + 6
20. 9,000,000 + 900,000 + 90,000 + 9,000 + 900 + 90 + 9

Page 9

1.	435	11.	46,987
2.	57	12.	511,300
3.	989	13.	206,978
4.	33,000	14.	44,255
5.	6,005	15.	11,601
6.	2,079	16.	349,003
7.	7,845	17.	72,165
8.	9,413	18.	836,72
9.	602,011	19.	289,06
10.	73,124	20.	100,90

Word Problem c

Page 10

1. one hundred sixty-eight
2. two hundred sixty-two
3. five hundred six
4. seven hundred twenty
5. one thousand, two hundred forty-six
6. three thousand, four hundred five
7. nineteen thousand, one hundred seventeen
8. twenty-three thousand, three hundred forty
9. forty-five thousand, one hundred three
10. forty-three thousand, nine hundred seventy-eight
11. ninety thousand, three
12. one hundred sixty thousand, five hundred nineteen
13. seven hundred four thousand, two hundred thirty
14. five hundred sixty-nine thousand, one hundred two
15. eighteen thousand, four hundred seventy-three
16. two hundred forty-five thousand, two hundred forty-six
17. eighty-three thousand, nine hundred
18. nine hundred sixty-seven thousand, five hundred eleven
19. thirteen thousand, nine hundred ninety-four
20. eight hundred eighty thousand, three hundred twelve

Page 11

1.	60	14.	7,200
2.	3,630	15.	700
3.	10	16.	3,200
4.	3,900	17.	0
5.	54,210	18.	3,300
6.	34,090	19.	6,400
7.	5,220	20.	8,300
8.	320	21.	800
9.	20	22.	300
		23.	14,200
			1,700
			4,000
			10,000

D1088836

27. 8,000   **32.** 203,000
28. 5,000   **33.** 3,000
29. 16,000   **34.** 35,000
30. 8,000   **35.** 1,000
31. 29,000   **36.** 1,000
Word Problem 55,000

Page 12
1. 1   2   7   14 15
      14 2 11   8 10
       4 9 10   10   5
2. 11 13 11 12 11
       9 9 12 7 11
      13 8 5 7 11
3. 14 9 8 9 13
      14 10 13 13 8
      10 15 4 9 6
4. 10 6 11 16 16
       5 7 8 4 10
       7 17 11 11 3
5. 5 7 16 14 10
       8 3 7 9 13
       9 15 6 14 1

Page 13
1. 29 19 37 17 29
      61 74 42
2. 90 108 153 115 86
     124 151 58
3. 926 714 875 1,228 864
     1,673 92 161
4. 11 11 6 19 12
      17 19 17
5. 172 190 143 216 114
     126 186 195
6. 1,112 1,446 2,234 1,024 1,620
     1,104 886 925
Calculator 623

Page 14
1. 5   **14.** 10
2. 5   **15.** 0
3. 1   **16.** 263
4. 4   **17.** 342
5. 1   **18.** 132
6. 3   **19.** 120
7. 0   **20.** 433
8. 8   **21.** 475
9. 7   **22.** 532
10. 1   **23.** 182
11. 10   **24.** 721
12. 11   **25.** 635
13. 11   **26.** 4,234

27. 4,221   **32.** 1,234
28. 2,311   **33.** 4,268
29. 4,001   **34.** 1,125
30. 601   **35.** 5,354
31. 5,322

Page 15
1. 19   **16.** 91
2. 29   **17.** 89
3. 64   **18.** 381
4. 18   **19.** 137
5. 79   **20.** 192
6. 12   **21.** 2,488
7. 19   **22.** 5,379
8. 109   **23.** 7,278
9. 548   **24.** 6,500
10. 689   **25.** 549
11. 809   **26.** 2,449
12. 515   **27.** 6,299
13. 699   **28.** 109
14. 199   **29.** 798
15. 397   **30.** 3,635
Word Problem 378

Page 16
1. 9   1 18 19 17
      38 27
2. 9 28 28   3   9
      18 48
3. 29 67 52 151 36
     2,040 4
4. 288 679 713 1,340 6
     137 439
5. 452 28 41 474 989
     832 1,217
6. 131 539 112 26 9,904
     3,173 5,461
7. 930 3,909 1,049 1,274 393
     789 3,682
8. 4,035 8,601 4,169 7,471 2,840
     5,093 889
9. 6,592 7,889 3,090 6,856 2,618
     4,788 1,098
10. 352 1,237 1,460 300 6,434
     370 2,423

Page 17
1. 50   **7.** 580
2. 900   **8.** 320
3. 240   **9.** 850
4. 120   **10.** 40
5. 150   **11.** 300
6. 200   **12.** 60

13. 10   **18.** 4,200 miles
14. 500   **19.** 40 years
15. 50   **20.** 3,400 people
16. 100
17. $70
Calculator 3,700 feet

Page 18
1. 12   **24.** 504
2. 42   **25.** 76
3. 30   **26.** 315
4. 64   **27.** 330
5. 24   **28.** 148
6. 56   **29.** 154
7. 63   **30.** 504
8. 48   **31.** 267
9. 14   **32.** 423
10. 20   **33.** 306
11. 0   **34.** 174
12. 81   **35.** 576
13. 25   **36.** 455
14. 27   **37.** 96
15. 36   **38.** 117
16. 32   **39.** 111
17. 15   **40.** 246
18. 45   **41.** 200
19. 14   **42.** 195
20. 32   **43.** 210
21. 24   **44.** 248
22. 45   **45.** 504
23. 204
Calculator $216.00

Page 19
1. 625   **16.** 2,316
2. 442   **17.** 8,736
3. 1,679   **18.** 8,140
4. 3,854   **19.** 3,124
5. 1,218   **20.** 19,529
6. 6,188   **21.** 31,239
7. 1,176   **22.** 14,586
8. 1,935   **23.** 11,845
9. 3,021   **24.** 39,355
10. 3,584 **25.** 102,102
11. 4,692 **26.** 69,524
12. 1,955 **27.** 396,808
13. 12,064 **28.** 72,705
14. 21,099 **29.** 301,670
15. 10,317 **30.** 515,036

Page 20

1. 7,660	**16.** 163,600
2. 22,100	**17.** 279,500
3. 21,690	**18.** 213,300
4. 32,880	**19.** 180,900
5. 20,430	**20.** 343,000
6. 17,100	**21.** 50,400
7. 31,320	**22.** 241,200
8. 14,560	**23.** 347,200
9. 16,530	**24.** 228,900
10. 12,780	**25.** 153,500
11. 319,200	**26.** 372,000
12. 759,600	**27.** 472,000
13. 275,800	**28.** 724,500
14. 298,000	**29.** 525,000
15. 320,500	**30.** 186,900

Calculator 356,000

Page 21

1. 71,440	**14.** 74,774
2. 257,682	**15.** 544,260
3. 148,512	**16.** 31,552,010
4. 69,525	**17.** 16,720,000
5. 415,291	**18.** 23,987,880
6. 146,046	**19.** 27,434,700
7. 246,442	**20.** 15,201,000
8. 342,538	**21.** 1,006,009
9. 329,058	**22.** 9,855,030
10. 89,486	**23.** 6,321,960
11. 257,298	**24.** 72,104,032
12. 621,270	**25.** 74,711,120
13. 202,521	

Page 22

1. 144 228 576 84
531 456 0

2. 2,064 3,969 2,348
1,906 1,887 1,872
690

3. 2,565 2,520 6,660
4,056 420 4,268
2,625

4. 1,535 2,430 1,804
3,618 1,515 5,642
8,172

5. 1,440 450 4,130
10,640 22,600 17,052
57,470

6. 40,725 23,780 31,408
57,960 8,487 1,144
54,280

7. 8,820 64,200 29,984
12,546 24,790 17,040
15,280

8. 94,518 195,348 61,950
62,400 243,024 241,891
77,824

9. 23,381 362,970 263,500
64,965 98,946 644,742
55,328

Word Problem 2,684

Page 23

1. 3	**16.** 11
2. 3	**17.** 13
3. 5	**18.** 12
4. 5	**19.** 12
5. 9	**20.** 13
6. 8	**21.** 14
7. 8	**22.** 14
8. 16	**23.** 12
9. 24	**24.** 15
10. 11	**25.** 16
11. 12	**26.** 14
12. 9	**27.** 13
13. 7	**28.** 19
14. 11	**29.** 23
15. 7	**30.** 21

Page 24

1. 2 R22	**11.** 2R8
2. 3 R35	**12.** 14 R27
3. 12 R31	**13.** 14
4. 20 R2	**14.** 8 R37
5. 8 R7	**15.** 12 R16
6. 2 R1	**16.** 11 R70
7. 3 R17	**17.** 96
8. 9 R10	**18.** 119 R27
9. 22 R7	**19.** 28 R29
10. 45 R2	**20.** 270 R9

Word Problem 13; 5 eggs left over

Page 25

1. 608 pounds
2. 127 cans
3. 1,071 miles
4. 164 gallons
5. 29 gallons
6. 52 weeks
7. 56 hours per week; 8 per day
8. 140 papers
9. 42 tulips
10. 87 computers; 48 printers

Page 26

1. 39 R25
2. 39
3. 27
4. 80
5. 45
6. 204
7. addition, subtraction; yes
8. addition, division; 50
9. multiplication, subtraction; 390
10. multiplication, subtraction; 1, 428

Page 27

1. c	**11.** c
2. a	**12.** c
3. b	**13.** a
4. b	**14.** c
5. b	**15.** d
6. c	**16.** b
7. b	**17.** b
8. a	**18.** a
9. d	**19.** b
10. c	**20.** a

Page 28

1. $\frac{3}{6}$	**5.** $\frac{3}{10}$
2. $\frac{3}{10}$	**6.** $\frac{1}{9}$
3. $\frac{2}{12}$	**7.** $\frac{5}{7}$
4. $\frac{2}{13}$	**8.** $\frac{10}{40}$

Page 29

1. $\frac{4}{8}$	**7.** $\frac{8}{20}$
2. $\frac{3}{8}$	**8.** $\frac{13}{32}$
3. $\frac{5}{12}$	**9.** $\frac{3}{8}$
4. $\frac{12}{32}$	**10.** $\frac{8}{8}$
5. $\frac{5}{8}$	**11.** $\frac{5}{12}$
6. $\frac{4}{8}$	**12.** $\frac{3}{8}$

Page 30

Shapes should be shaded according to directions.

Page 31

1. twenty-two eightieths
2. twelve sixtieths
3. two seventeenths
4. eighteen twenty-sevenths
5. five ninetieths
6. seventy one-hundredths

7. eight thirtieths
8. seventeen seventieths
9. fifty-five sixty-ninths
10. one ninety-ninth
11. thirty-four forty-eighths
12. seven one-hundredths

Page 32

1. 15
2. 18
3. 32
4. 18
5. 72
6. 16
7. 32
8. 12
9. 28
10. 143
11. 40
12. 64
13. 20
14. 42
15. 48

16. 46
17. 49
18. 24
19. 40
20. 24
21. 66
22. 33
23. 11
24. 75
25. 40
26. 25
27. 36
28. 9
29. 21
30. 25

Word Problem Gloria and Nancy

Page 33

1. $\frac{1}{5}$
2. $\frac{1}{5}$
3. $\frac{2}{3}$
4. $\frac{3}{4}$
5. $\frac{10}{11}$
6. $\frac{1}{2}$
7. $\frac{1}{4}$
8. $\frac{1}{4}$
9. $\frac{1}{3}$
10. $\frac{2}{3}$
11. $\frac{3}{7}$
12. $\frac{2}{5}$
13. $\frac{11}{20}$
14. $\frac{3}{11}$
15. $\frac{1}{5}$
16. $\frac{2}{5}$
17. $\frac{7}{8}$
18. $\frac{3}{4}$
19. $\frac{5}{6}$
20. $\frac{1}{10}$

21. $\frac{2}{7}$
22. $\frac{2}{11}$
23. $\frac{1}{11}$
24. $\frac{1}{3}$
25. $\frac{3}{7}$
26. $\frac{2}{5}$
27. $\frac{1}{2}$
28. $\frac{7}{11}$
29. $\frac{5}{19}$
30. $\frac{11}{13}$
31. $\frac{3}{16}$
32. $\frac{1}{5}$
33. $\frac{1}{7}$
34. $\frac{3}{11}$
35. $\frac{1}{7}$
36. $\frac{1}{9}$
37. $\frac{1}{2}$
38. $\frac{1}{3}$
39. $\frac{3}{10}$
40. $\frac{7}{8}$

Page 34

1. $\frac{5}{2}$
2. $\frac{16}{3}$
3. $\frac{23}{3}$
4. $\frac{33}{5}$
5. $\frac{11}{3}$
6. $\frac{21}{5}$
7. $\frac{37}{7}$
8. $\frac{13}{2}$
9. $\frac{27}{5}$
10. $\frac{57}{7}$

11. $\frac{75}{9}$
12. $\frac{38}{12}$
13. $\frac{68}{11}$
14. $\frac{29}{5}$
15. $\frac{93}{10}$
16. $\frac{146}{12}$
17. $\frac{67}{10}$
18. $\frac{93}{11}$
19. $\frac{8}{5}$
20. $\frac{39}{5}$

Word Problem $4\frac{1}{2}$ feet

Page 35

1. $2\frac{6}{11}$
2. 19
3. $19\frac{1}{2}$
4. $1\frac{2}{3}$
5. $3\frac{4}{5}$
6. $3\frac{1}{5}$
7. $3\frac{5}{8}$
8. $4\frac{9}{11}$
9. $3\frac{2}{5}$
10. $7\frac{2}{5}$
11. 6
12. $6\frac{4}{7}$
13. 8
14. $5\frac{3}{10}$
15. $3\frac{4}{7}$

16. $5\frac{1}{2}$
17. $2\frac{2}{15}$
18. $1\frac{12}{17}$
19. 4
20. 3
21. $7\frac{7}{8}$
22. $4\frac{11}{12}$
23. $6\frac{2}{3}$
24. 8
25. $7\frac{1}{10}$
26. $5\frac{5}{6}$
27. 9
28. $3\frac{4}{13}$
29. $2\frac{9}{11}$
30. $3\frac{1}{2}$

Page 36

1. $15\frac{1}{2}$
2. 19
3. 7
4. $12\frac{1}{2}$
5. $40\frac{1}{5}$
6. $17\frac{1}{7}$
7. $29\frac{1}{5}$
8. $14\frac{1}{6}$
9. $28\frac{1}{5}$
10. $16\frac{4}{7}$
11. $20\frac{1}{2}$
12. $24\frac{1}{4}$

13. $34\frac{1}{3}$
14. $3\frac{2}{5}$
15. $14\frac{1}{16}$
16. $10\frac{2}{7}$
17. 19
18. 11
19. $10\frac{3}{10}$
20. $73\frac{1}{5}$
21. 14
22. $13\frac{1}{7}$
23. $17\frac{4}{7}$
24. $7\frac{1}{8}$

Word Problem 25

Page 37

1. $\frac{5}{7}$
2. $\frac{9}{11}$
3. $1\frac{1}{13}$
4. $1\frac{17}{15}$
5. $8\frac{2}{11}$
6. $11\frac{10}{13}$
7. 20
8. $7\frac{1}{7}$

9. $9\frac{14}{15}$
10. $8\frac{5}{18}$
11. 11
12. $8\frac{1}{2}$
13. $11\frac{7}{11}$
14. $5\frac{11}{12}$
15. 12

Page 38

1. $15\frac{19}{36}$
2. $21\frac{11}{25}$
3. $7\frac{1}{2}$
4. $9\frac{17}{18}$
5. $34\frac{13}{32}$
6. $2\frac{17}{52}$
7. $8\frac{7}{74}$
8. $11\frac{1}{2}$

9. $7\frac{13}{15}$
10. $24\frac{17}{30}$
11. $10\frac{1}{21}$
12. $17\frac{26}{35}$
13. $7\frac{8}{39}$
14. $42\frac{7}{18}$
15. $11\frac{10}{27}$

Word Problem $5\frac{13}{15}$ gallons

Page 39

1. $11\frac{11}{14}$
2. $9\frac{7}{12}$
3. $44\frac{1}{10}$
4. $10\frac{13}{21}$
5. $8\frac{7}{10}$
6. $7\frac{19}{24}$
7. $12\frac{7}{12}$
8. $10\frac{19}{42}$
9. $6\frac{19}{30}$
10. $17\frac{5}{33}$

11. $5\frac{19}{45}$
12. $6\frac{37}{55}$
13. $21\frac{9}{44}$
14. $3\frac{1}{2}$
15. $6\frac{29}{40}$
16. $7\frac{11}{12}$
17. $14\frac{1}{30}$
18. $8\frac{1}{6}$
19. $8\frac{43}{56}$
20. $9\frac{19}{45}$

Page 40

1. $1\frac{1}{4}$
2. $6\frac{1}{6}$
3. $9\frac{3}{8}$
4. $6\frac{5}{8}$
5. $6\frac{1}{10}$
6. $6\frac{1}{16}$
7. $28\frac{4}{15}$
8. $22\frac{3}{26}$
9. $33\frac{7}{26}$
10. $34\frac{6}{11}$

11. $60\frac{1}{12}$
12. $12\frac{1}{5}$
13. $2\frac{5}{8}$
14. $5\frac{10}{17}$
15. $1\frac{1}{2}$
16. $19\frac{1}{14}$
17. $69\frac{2}{13}$
18. $5\frac{4}{45}$
19. $2\frac{3}{20}$
20. $9\frac{2}{57}$

Word Problem $5\frac{5}{8}$ quarts

Page 41

1. $\frac{17}{24}$
2. $\frac{1}{6}$
3. $\frac{19}{36}$
4. $\frac{13}{35}$
5. $\frac{11}{24}$
6. $33\frac{3}{10}$
7. $\frac{3}{8}$
8. $39\frac{7}{24}$
9. $39\frac{2}{3}$
10. $18\frac{23}{30}$
11. $2\frac{13}{22}$
12. $10\frac{7}{15}$
13. $5\frac{20}{33}$
14. $37\frac{7}{34}$

15. $8\frac{1}{2}$
16. $35\frac{17}{57}$
17. $19\frac{16}{45}$
18. $19\frac{13}{28}$
19. $8\frac{29}{48}$
20. $18\frac{61}{110}$
21. $13\frac{7}{24}$
22. $6\frac{1}{30}$
23. $7\frac{3}{8}$
24. $12\frac{9}{40}$
25. $9\frac{7}{24}$

Page 42

1. $3\frac{14}{17}$
2. $11\frac{2}{5}$
3. $11\frac{19}{21}$
4. $4\frac{17}{18}$
5. $1\frac{3}{11}$
6. $13\frac{7}{24}$
7. $14\frac{3}{5}$
8. $5\frac{10}{11}$
9. $48\frac{6}{7}$
10. $49\frac{34}{45}$
11. $10\frac{17}{36}$
12. $6\frac{6}{7}$

Word Problem $3\frac{1}{3}$ yards

Page 43

1. $\frac{10}{11}$
2. $\frac{16}{27}$
3. $\frac{1}{4}$
4. $\frac{2}{5}$
5. $\frac{13}{16}$
6. $\frac{5}{8}$
7. $\frac{5}{16}$
8. $\frac{3}{4}$
9. $\frac{2}{9}$
10. $\frac{10}{21}$
11. $\frac{5}{13}$
12. $\frac{4}{7}$
13. $\frac{2}{3}$
14. $\frac{1}{2}$
15. $\frac{5}{11}$
16. $\frac{3}{13}$
17. $\frac{1}{27}$
18. $\frac{1}{8}$
19. $\frac{1}{4}$
20. $\frac{1}{26}$
21. $\frac{1}{16}$
22. $\frac{1}{18}$
23. $\frac{1}{4}$
24. $\frac{1}{12}$

Page 44

1. $\frac{18}{5}$
2. $\frac{28}{6}$
3. $\frac{35}{12}$
4. $\frac{56}{5}$
5. $\frac{79}{10}$
6. $\frac{32}{12}$
7. $10\frac{6}{13}$
8. $\frac{17}{9}$
9. $\frac{95}{17}$
10. $\frac{35}{9}$
11. $2\frac{14}{15}$
12. $7\frac{2}{3}$
13. $21\frac{3}{20}$
14. $8\frac{3}{4}$
15. $\frac{1}{6}$
16. $5\frac{1}{3}$
17. 6
18. 26
19. $1\frac{6}{7}$
20. $7\frac{1}{3}$
21. $\frac{4}{7}$
22. $3\frac{13}{15}$
23. 27
24. 1
25. 8
26. $4\frac{12}{25}$
27. $9\frac{1}{7}$
28. 9

Word Problem $1\frac{5}{8}$ hours

Page 45

1. $\frac{35}{36}$
2. $\frac{1}{4}$
3. $\frac{11}{12}$
4. $1\frac{1}{13}$
5. $1\frac{1}{7}$
6. $\frac{2}{3}$
7. $1\frac{1}{14}$
8. $\frac{2}{3}$
9. $1\frac{1}{10}$
10. $\frac{1}{6}$
11. $\frac{2}{3}$
12. $\frac{9}{13}$
13. $\frac{11}{3}$
14. $\frac{24}{77}$
15. $\frac{8}{15}$
16. $1\frac{1}{9}$
17. $\frac{4}{11}$
18. $3\frac{3}{7}$
19. 1
20. $\frac{77}{152}$

Page 46

1. $1\frac{7}{8}$
2. $\frac{17}{26}$
3. $\frac{16}{75}$
4. $1\frac{3}{22}$
5. $1\frac{5}{9}$
6. $10\frac{2}{3}$
7. 1
8. $1\frac{3}{7}$
9. $\frac{13}{30}$
10. $1\frac{29}{49}$
11. $3\frac{1}{2}$
12. $\frac{1}{2}$
13. $\frac{2}{3}$
14. $1\frac{6}{7}$
15. $1\frac{1}{30}$
16. $1\frac{2}{3}$
17. $\frac{7}{24}$
18. $\frac{24}{29}$
19. $1\frac{1}{3}$
20. $\frac{27}{70}$
21. $3\frac{1}{3}$

Word Problem 10

Page 47

1. <
2. =
3. >
4. >
5. >
6. <
7. >
8. >
9. <
10. >
11. >
12. >
13. =
14. >
15. <
16. =
17. <
18. <
19. =
20. <
21. <
22. <
23. >
24. >

Page 48

1. $25\frac{2}{3}$ pounds
2. $\frac{3}{8}$ tank
3. $4\frac{1}{12}$ miles
4. $22\frac{3}{4}$ hours
5. 80 students
6. $16\frac{4}{7}$ pounds
7. $18\frac{1}{3}$ bushels
8. $9.00 per hour
9. $\frac{13}{28}$ acre
10. No

Page 49

1. d
2. a
3. a
4. b
5. c
6. b
7. a
8. d
9. c
10. a
11. a
12. c
13. d
14. c
15. b
16. b
17. c
18. a
19. d
20. d

Page 50

1. two and six hundred five thousandths
2. fourteen and seven hundredths
3. one thousand seven hundred twenty-three ten-thousandths
4. one tenth
5. fourteen and two tenths
6. one and six tenths
7. seventeen and three thousandths
8. one and seventy-seven hundredths
9. twenty-nine and one tenth
10. twenty-two hundredths
11. twenty-two hundredths
12. one hundredth

Page 51

1. 6.24
2. 16.016
3. 0.12
4. 500.09
5. 200.0003
6. 56.0411
7. 0.00341
8. 60.00012
9. 0.009
10. 0.7045
11. 0.13
12. 15.00018
13. 9.00008
14. 9.0008
15. 0.52
16. 0.075

Page 52

1. >
2. >
3. >
4. >
5. >
6. >
7. >
8. >
9. <
10. >
11. >
12. <
13. >
14. <
15. >
16. 1.7, 0.162, 0.1073
17. 5.6, 5.551, 4.823
18. 7.03, 0.704, 0.0703
19. 17, 1.7, .701
20. 1.5, 0.51, 0.502
21. 0.8081, 0.808, 0.8018
22. .7714, 67, 0.6602
23. 8.8, 8.088, 8

Page 53
1. .60
2. .125
3. .75
4. .875
5. .70
6. .50
7. .65
8. .625
9. .25
10. .20

Calculator $23,616

Page 54
1. 4.6
2. 6.3
3. 0.8
4. 1
5. 0.1
6. 96
7. 0
8. 126.2
9. 5.02
10. 3.79
11. 0.41
12. 1.06
13. 0.31
14. 0.20
15. 2.12
16. 285.09
17. 0.093
18. 0.629
19. 0.129
20. 9.003
21. 5.168
22. 28.412
23. 0.625
24. 0.008

Page 55
1. 6.36
2. 17.7
3. 2.69
4. 148.241
5. 27.7
6. 12.35
7. 10.81
8. 23.1
9. 12.75
10. 27.31
11. 16.31
12. 14.121
13. 7.5

Calculator 7.032

Page 56
1. 1.75
2. 3.31
3. 30.2
4. 3.86
5. 3.77
6. 11.25
7. 17.1
8. 25.95
9. 4.44
10. 1.909
11. 2.952
12. 6.28
13. 34.9379
14. 3.9
15. 0.7

Page 57
1. 9.03
2. 1.476
3. 7.32
4. 18.69
5. 5.27
6. 0.7695
7. 22.317
8. 5.43
9. 52.9
10. 197.82
11. 1.7241
12. 57.456
13. 4.3569
14. 105.472
15. 61.705
16. 186.345
17. 2.4662
18. 8.1911

Calculator $706

Page 58
1. .023
2. .0638
3. .0504
4. .001242
5. .003115
6. .02769
7. .02355
8. .0876
9. .005535
10. .000025
11. .01255
12. .02808
13. .00109
14. .000696
15. .00118
16. .02472
17. .01305
18. .000575
19. .000066
20. .00987

Page 59
1. 1.9
2. 2.5
3. 1.8
4. 2.51
5. 3.1
6. 0.23
7. 4.01
8. 5.55
9. 0.93
10. 2.6
11. 4.2
12. 1.03
13. .62
14. 1.01
15. 2.63
16. 0.11
17. 0.231
18. 0.035
19. 0.089
20. 0.112

Calculator 4.5 tickets

Page 60
1. 1.44
2. 1.7
3. 2.6
4. 3.7
5. 2.9
6. 1.04
7. 0.025
8. 0.17
9. 5.1
10. 0.034
11. 0.046
12. 0.135
13. 1.43
14. 21.3
15. 19.2
16. 4.5
17. 2.3
18. 5.1
19. 0.002
20. 0.013

Page 61
1. 300
2. 400
3. 210
4. 90
5. 120
6. 640
7. 2,120
8. 430
9. 510
10. 810
11. 910
12. 1,230
13. 1,730
14. 220
15. 350
16. 1,220
17. 210
18. 230
19. 330
20. 210
21. 320
22. 210
23. 1,620
24. 240

Page 62
1. 2,630
2. 82,900
3. 39,000
4. 621,300
5. 41,200
6. 2,650
7. 23,200
8. 2,000
9. 91,110
10. 4,010
11. 380
12. 68
13. 29
14. 7,900
15. 1,200
16. 3,000
17. 54
18. 39
19. 2,340
20. 100

Page 63
1. c
2. a
3. c
4. c
5. d
6. a
7. c
8. d
9. b
10. c
11. a
12. c
13. c
14. c
15. c
16. b
17. b
18. d
19. c
20. b

Page 64
1. $\frac{1}{2}$
2. $\frac{3}{4}$
3. $\frac{3}{2}$
4. $\frac{2}{1}$
5. $\frac{4}{3}$
6. $\frac{1}{2}$
7. $\frac{4}{7}$
8. $\frac{7}{6}$
9. $\frac{1}{1}$
10. $\frac{7}{3}$

Page 65
1. $\frac{1}{2}$
2. $\frac{2}{3}$
3. $\frac{1}{4}$
4. $\frac{2}{1}$
5. $\frac{4}{3}$
6. $\frac{4}{1}$
7. $\frac{4}{7}$
8. $\frac{1}{1}$
9. $\frac{1}{6}$
10. $\frac{3}{2}$
11. $\frac{4}{1}$
12. $\frac{1}{4}$
13. $\frac{4}{5}$
14. $\frac{4}{3}$
15. $\frac{2}{1}$
16. $\frac{1}{3}$
17. $\frac{3}{2}$
18. $\frac{3}{2}$
19. $\frac{4}{3}$
20. $\frac{3}{4}$
21. $\frac{5}{4}$
22. $\frac{1}{1}$

Word Problem a

Page 66
1. $\frac{3}{2}$
2. $\frac{1}{4}$
3. $\frac{80}{3}$
4. $\frac{2}{1}$
5. $\frac{5}{2}$
6. $\frac{1}{1}$
7. $\frac{4}{3}$

8. $\frac{2}{5}$
9. $\frac{4}{1}$
10. $\frac{40}{1}$
11. $\frac{3}{4}$
12. $\frac{5}{28}$
13. $\frac{1}{4}$
14. $\frac{48}{1}$
Word Problem $\frac{3}{4}$

Page 67
1. =
2. =
3. =
4. ≠
5. ≠
6. =
7. ≠
8. =
9. ≠
10. ≠
11. =
12. ≠
13. ≠
14. ≠
15. ≠
16. =

Page 68
1. 6
2. $9\frac{3}{5}$
3. 120
4. $9\frac{3}{5}$
5. 5
6. $12\frac{1}{2}$
Word Problem $4\frac{3}{5}$ hours

Page 69
1. 4
2. 9
3. 12
4. 10
5. 2
6. $3\frac{1}{5}$
7. 45
8. 27
9. $4\frac{1}{2}$
10. $4\frac{4}{5}$
11. $7\frac{1}{2}$
12. $7\frac{1}{2}$
13. 48
14. 195
15. 5
16. 39
17. 120
18. 7
19. $12\frac{1}{2}$
20. 25
21. 9
Word Problem 8
Page 70
1. $1.26
2. $3.38
3. $4.47
4. $2.07
5. $4.79
6. $1.50

Page 71
1. $7.44
2. $3.84
3. $6.23
4. $3.50
5. $2.24
6. $1.99
7. $8.09
8. $1.19
9. 2 pounds
10. 40 miles

Page 72
1. 144 miles
2. $1\frac{1}{2}$ pounds of peanuts
3. $\frac{3}{4}$ pint of yellow
4. $7.92
5. 136 km
6. 224 miles
7. 388 men
8. 15 lemons
9. $8.40
10. 16 counselors

Page 73
1. $\frac{32}{100}$ or 32%
2. $\frac{32}{100}$ or 32%
3. $\frac{27}{100}$ or 27%
4. $\frac{60}{100}$ or 60%
5. $\frac{18}{100}$ or 18%
6. $\frac{2}{100}$ or 2%
7. $\frac{37}{100}$ or 37%
8. $\frac{56}{100}$ or 56%
9. $\frac{10}{100}$ or 10%

Page 74
1. 80%
2. 30%
3. 60%
4. $87\frac{1}{2}$%
5. $33\frac{1}{3}$%
6. $57\frac{1}{7}$%
7. 90%
8. $66\frac{2}{3}$%
9. $16\frac{2}{3}$%
Calculator $33\frac{1}{3}$%

Page 75
1. 72%
2. 39%
3. 7%
4. 54%
5. 26%
6. 112%
7. 140%
8. 81%
9. 165%
10. 43%
11. 2%
12. 74.6%
13. 2.6%
14. 110%
15. 1%
16. 10.3%
17. 124%
18. 33%
19. 700%
20. 3.4%

21. 204%
22. 23%
23. 120%
24. 220%
25. 3%
26. 11.1%
27. 1,120%
28. 25%
29. .46
30. .6
31. .08
32. .56
33. .8
34. 2.54
35. .01
36. 1.83
37. .92
38. .012
39. 1.2
40. .175
41. .02
42. .00021
43. .022
44. 3.52
45. .05
46. .0311
47. .0011
48. .96
49. .013
50. .123
51. .41
52. .01023
53. .0222
54. .0003
55. .0001
56. .00019

Page 76
1. $\frac{7}{25}$
2. $\frac{2}{25}$
3. $\frac{11}{100}$
4. $\frac{11}{25}$
5. $1\frac{1}{20}$
6. $\frac{17}{20}$
7. $\frac{18}{25}$
8. $\frac{1}{40}$
9. $\frac{1}{3}$
10. $\frac{7}{50}$
11. $\frac{7}{100}$
12. $\frac{11}{60}$
13. $1\frac{1}{5}$
14. $\frac{12}{25}$
15. $\frac{1}{8}$
16. $\frac{1}{50}$
17. .75, 75%
18. $\frac{9}{25}$, 36%
19. $\frac{4}{25}$, .16
20. $.66\frac{2}{3}$, $66\frac{2}{3}$%
21. $\frac{2}{25}$, .08
22. .65, 65%
23. $\frac{2}{5}$, 40%
24. $\frac{37}{250}$, 14.8%
25. .175, 17.5%
26. $\frac{1}{2}$, .5
27. $2\frac{3}{5}$, 260%
28. $.83\frac{1}{3}$, $83\frac{1}{3}$%
29. $\frac{12}{25}$, .48
30. $\frac{1}{20}$, 5%
31. $\frac{11}{20}$, .55
32. $\frac{13}{50}$, 26%
33. .6, 60%

34. $\frac{7}{20}$, .35
Calculator $\frac{1}{6}$ real fruit juice

Page 77
1. 12.6
2. 1.2
3. 32.4
4. 14.4
5. 7
6. .06
7. 23.2
8. 2.4
9. 48
10. 27
11. $7\frac{3}{5}$
12. $49\frac{3}{5}$
13. 3
14. 7
15. $11\frac{1}{5}$
16. 3
17. 170
18. 2

Page 78
1. $4.99
2. $36.75
3. $18.24
4. $6.09
5. $1.92
6. $.46
7. $9.51
8. $196.64
9. $2.25
10. $55.50
11. $29.93
12. $9.52

Page 79
1. $30.12; $95.38
2. $.15; $1.74
3. $33.28; $174.72
4. $6.50; $26.00
5. $5.28; $12.32
6. $70.02; $318.98
7. $6.07; $31.88
8. $4.65; $13.95
9. $10.46; $19.43
Calculator $1,056.00

Page 80
1. 5:35
2. 6:10
3. 3:38
4. 7:51
5. 4:16
6. 3:59
7. 7:59
8. 5:33
9. 5:56

Word Problem 7:38

Page 81
1. 3:15
2. 2:46
3. 0:48
4. 1:13
5. 2:45
6. 1:56
7. 3:15
8. 5:13
9. 3:20
10. 4:20

Page 82
1. 3 in.
2. $3\frac{1}{2}$ in.
3. $3\frac{7}{8}$ in.
4. $1\frac{3}{8}$ in.
5. $2\frac{5}{8}$ in.
6. $3\frac{7}{16}$ in.
7. $3\frac{7}{8}$ in.
8. 4in.
9. $5\frac{1}{4}$ in.
10. $5\frac{9}{16}$ in.
11. $2\frac{7}{16}$ in.

Page 83
1. 6 feet
2. 5,280 yards
3. 84 inches
4. 63,360 inches
5. 49 yards
6. 21,120 feet
7. 4 feet
8. 2 miles
9. 8 yards
10. 276 inches
11. 60 inches
12. 27 feet
13. 168 inches
14. 13 feet
15. 10 miles
16. 216 inches
Calculator 30 miles

Page 84
1. 3 feet 10 inches
2. 4 yards 5 inches
3. 6 yards 3 inches
4. 16 feet 11 inches
5. 2 yards 2 feet 10 inches
6. 1 yard 33 inches
7. 12 yards 5 inches
8. 1 foot 3 inches

Page 85
1. 8 sq. in.
2. $2\frac{7}{16}$ sq. in.
3. 6.72 sq. in.
4. $3\frac{1}{2}$ sq. ft.
5. $1\frac{1}{2}$ sq. in.
6. $16\frac{1}{2}$ sq. ft.
7. .516 sq. ft.
8. 1.26 sq. in.
9. 2 sq. ft.
10. 9 sq. in.
11. 6.72 sq. in.
12. 1.44 sq. in.
13. 1 sq. in
14. $\frac{3}{4}$ sq. in.

15. 6 sq. in.
Calculator d

Page 86
1. 16 cu. in.
2. .48 cu. ft.
3. 72 cu. in.
4. 2,016 cu. in.
5. 14 cu. in.
6. 1,920 cu. in.
7. 11.2 cu. in.
8. 252 cu. in.
9. 21 cu. in.
10. 16 cu. in.
11. 38.4 cu. in.
12. 24 cu. ft.
13. 8 cu. in.
14. 3.6 cu. in.
15. 35 cu. in.
16. 90 cu. in.

Page 87
1. 8 cm or 81 mm
2. 9 cm or 85 mm
3. 6 cm or 64 mm
4. 10 cm or 98 mm
5. 11 cm or 113 mm
6. 6 cm or 60 mm
7. 10 cm or 97 mm
8. 8 cm or 75 mm
9. 12 cm or 117 mm

Page 88
1. 4.8 cm
2. 2,500 cm
3. 6,000 m
4. 250 mm
5. 52 mm
6. .0042 km
7. 700 cm
8. 450 cm
9. .42 m
10. 4,200 cm
11. 3,070 mm
12. 453 mm
13. 7 mm
14. .25 km
15. 4.6 km
16. .42 mm
17. 2.4 cm
18. 48 mm
19. .65 m
20. 72 cm
21. 600 m
22. 39 cm
23. 52.3 cm
24. 102 mm
25. 595 mm
26. 10.1 cm
27. 609.7 cm
28. 472 cm
29. 308.5 cm

Calculator Gina

Page 89

1. 6.36 cm^2
2. 6.72 cm^2
3. 344 mm^2
4. 3.2 cm^2
5. 276 mm^2
6. 64 mm^2
7. 184 mm^2
8. 1.28 cm^2
9. 4.08 m^2
10. 26.01 cm^2
11. 5.29 cm^2
12. 33.6 cm^2
13. 378 mm^2
14. .48 cm^2
15. 9.84 cm^2

Page 90

1. 96 oz.
2. 24 pt.
3. 4 qt.
4. 40 c.
5. 6 pt.
6. 1,280 oz.
7. 13$\frac{1}{2}$ pt.
8. 56 c.
9. 3 pt.
10. 2$\frac{1}{4}$ gal.
11. 22 qt.
12. 35 oz.
13. 24 oz.
14. 16$\frac{1}{2}$ qt.
15. 18 qt.
16. 5$\frac{3}{4}$ qt.
17. 50 pt.
18. 160 oz.

Calculator 4

Page 91

1. 31.4 in.
2. 50.24 cm
3. 18.84 cm
4. 28.26 mm
5. 21.98 cm
6. 6.28 mm
7. 81.64 mm
8. 62.8 mm
9. 113.04 in.
10. 69.08 m
11. 62.8 cm
12. 75.36 in.
13. 94.2 mm
14. 100.48 cm
15. 21.98 in.
16. 34.54 in.

Page 92

1. 12.56 sq. in.
2. 3.14 cm^2
3. 28.26 mm^2
4. 78.5 cm^2
5. .0314 cm^2
6. .5024 cm^2
7. 1,256 mm^2
8. 55.3896 sq. in.
9. 706.5 cm^2
10. 254.34 sq. in.
11. $\frac{22}{7}$ = 3$\frac{1}{7}$ m^2
12. 154 mm^2
13. 38$\frac{1}{2}$ sq. in.
14. 28$\frac{2}{7}$ mm^2
15. 1,386 cm^2
16. $\frac{22}{28}$ = $\frac{11}{14}$ m^2
17. 17$\frac{1}{9}$ sq. in.
18. 50$\frac{2}{7}$ cm^2
19. 314$\frac{2}{7}$ mm^2
20. 1$\frac{3}{11}$ sq. in.

Page 93

1. 1,008 cm^3
2. 512 cm^3
3. 2,200 cm^3
4. 4,500 cm^3
5. 3,360 mm^3
6. 360 mm^3
7. 6,600 cm^3
8. 3,200 cm^3
9. 3,840 mm^3
10. 4,200 mm3
11. 576 cm^3
12. 1,620 cm^3
13. 1,008 cm^3
14. 480 mm^3
15. 240 mm^3
16. 5,760 cm^3

Page 94

1. c
2. c
3. a
4. a
5. b
6. d
7. d
8. a
9. c
10. d
11. b
12. a
13. a
14. c
15. d
16. b
17. b
18. c
19. a
20. b

Page 95–96

1. b
2. d
3. b
4. c
5. d
6. c
7. a
8. b
9. c
10. b
11. b
12. d
13. a
14. c
15. c
16. a
17. a
18. b
19. d
20. c
21. d
22. c
23. c
24. a
25. d
26. b
27. c
28. d
29. a
30. a
31. d
32. b
33. d
34. c
35. d
36. d
37. a
38. b
39. d
40. a

Consumer Math

Page 5

1. 30.48	**7.** 8.9
2. 52.8	**8.** 15.7
3. 61.0	**9.** 1.86
4. 225.8	**10.** .83
5. 96.40	**11.** 19.01
6. 279.76	**12.** 5.24

Page 6

1. $192.60	**7.** $184.60
2. $280.00	**8.** $214.60
3. $168.00	**9.** $209.25
4. $290.00	**10.** $224.20
5. $144.20	**11.** $248.00
6. $207.00	

Page 7

12. $142.50	**17.** $170.00
13. $163.20	**18.** $405.00
14. $117.60	**19.** $92.00
15. $83.33	**20.** $85.10
16. $80.75	

Page 9

1. $184.00; $27.60; $211.60
2. $200.00; $60.00; $260.00
3. $193.60; $72.60; $266.20
4. $216.00; $54.00; $270.00
5. $204.00; $91.80; $295.80
6. $176.40; $14.70; $191.10
7. $268.00; $40.20; $308.20
8. $324.80; $121.80; $446.60
9. $275.50; $65.25; $340.75
10. $309.60
11. $504.00
12. $379.80
13. $273.60
14. $176.40
15. $352.80
16. $342.00
17. $331.20
18. $298.80
19. $478.40
20. $451.50
Calculator $411.75

Page 10

1. $5.16; $31.26
2. $114; $324
3. $80; $192.50
4. $2,865; $3,000
5. $1,080; $1,332
6. $492; $690

7. $440; $708
8. $252; $576.80
9. $228; $503.50
10. $220; $405.30

Page 11

11. $22.56	**16.** $3,270
12. $221.40	**17.** $8,680
13. $105	**18.** $56.80
14. $3,227.90	**19.** $9,600
15. $8,400	**20.** $189

Calculator Lia, $106.00

Page 12

1. $141.43
2. $243.20
3. $442.90
4. $232.48

Page 13

5. $310.00; $227.60
6. $180.00; $141.84
7. $177.80; $147.68
8. $163.84; $121.09
9. $178.00; $127.37
10. $203.00; $145.28
11. $210.70; $132.30
12. $202.50; $156.05
13. $177.60; $123.80
14. $262.00; $200.08
15. $224.20; $169.49
16. $276.90; $214.47
17. $641.05
18. $652.00
19. $93.62
20. $384.95

Page 14

1. 23.38	**14.** 9.38
2. 94.3	**15.** 9.42
3. 456.3	**16.** 139.9
4. 180.49	**17.** 12.8
5. 22.413	**18.** 10.3
6. 541.06	**19.** 22.3
7. 39.51	**20.** 6.69
8. 276.04	**21.** 3.96
9. 24.173	**22.** 102.2
10. 28.12	**23.** 2.65
11. 253.8	**24.** 4.74
12. 4.06	**25.** 27.18
13. 47.7	**26.** 197.6

Calculator $355.22

Page 15

1. 7	**9.** .72
2. 19	**10.** 4.69
3. 29	**11.** .08
4. 8	**12.** 24.00
5. .8	**13.** .10
6. 4.5	**14.** 15.68
7. .1	**15.** .04
8. 12.6	

Page 16

1. $55.70
2. $197.50
3. $249.05
4. $124.08
5. $426.01
6. $213.38

Page 17

7. 51-3829-70	$125.00
May 20, 97	$48.90
Bill Gerardi	$116.28
	$290.18
	$290.18

Page 18

8. June 15, 98
Steven Haar   175-08-612
One hundred twenty-five and
no/100
$125.00
Steven Haar (signature)
9. May 29, 99
Ann Kasper   314-30-697
Two hundred forty-five and
no/100
$245.00
Ann Kasper (signature)

Page 19

1. $10	**9.** $52
2. $72	**10.** $168
3. $26	**11.** $56.25
4. $110	**12.** $160
5. $320	**13.** $450
6. $210	**14.** $143
7. $37.50	**15.** $117.80
8. $136	**16.** $37.35

Page 20

17. $21
18. $22.50
19. $90
20. $270
21. $35.75
22. $980
23. $14.85
24. $93
25. $27.60
26. $337.50
27. $75.63
28. $40.50
29. $552
30. $45.90
Calculator $144

Page 21

1. $20.81
2. $1,061.21
3. $21.22
4. $1,082.43
5. $5.00; $505.00; $5.05; $510.05
6. $40.00; $2,040.00; $40.80; $2,080.80
7. $60.00; $4,060.00; $60.90; $4,120.90
8. $48.00; $2,448.00; $48.96; $2,496.96

Page 22

9. $721.16
10. $1,050.63
11. $2,706.08
12. $1,264.11
13. $1,824.75
14. $787.50
Calculator $4,329.73

Page 23

1. $533.30
2. $614.10
3. $1,180.87
4. $1,397.35
5. $578.37
6. $995.15

Page 24

7. $1,215.53
8. $678.50
9. $691.00
10. $766.00
11. $856.00
12. $771.00
13. $891.00
14. $796.00
15. $875.50

Page 25

1. 12.6
2. .306
3. .053
4. 163.74
5. 19.7
6. .436
7. 119.14
8. 1.86
9. 47.34
10. .56
11. .032
12. .0035

Page 27

1. 35.45
2. 23.9
3. 2.98
4. 36.2
5. .159
6. 32
7. 254
8. 427
9. 3.9
10. 1.6
11. .6
12. 1.7
13. 57
14. 3.6
15. 64
16. 5.2
17. 9.4
18. 40
19. 5.23
20. 73
21. .34
22. .153
23. 2
24. 410
25. .91
26. 456
27. 8.62
28. 3,562.50
Calculator 24 miles

Page 28

1. $224.95
2. $328.15

Page 29

3. Total deposit: $115.55
4. Total deposit: $394.65
5. Total deposit: $417.83
6. Total deposit: $882.15
7. Total deposit: $203.75
8. Total deposit: $651.50
Calculator $301.55

Page 31

1. Twenty and 75/100
2. One hundred twenty-five and no/100
3. Four hundred thirty-eight and 92/100
4. One thousand four hundred seventy-five and no/100
5. Twenty-four thousand two hundred and no/100
6. Jim's Auto Clinic
7. $45.00
8. tune-up and oil change
9. Karen Meushaw
10. yes

Page 32

1. April 21, 98
Mary's Beauty Shop
$25.00
Twenty-five and no/100
haircut
Margaret Allen (signature)

Page 33

2. May 12, 96
A-1 Repair Service
$85.75
Eighty-five and 75/100
VCR repair
Terri Smith (signature)
3. September 26, 96
Allied Auto Service
$137.50
One hundred thirty-seven and 50/100
auto repair
John Savarese (signature)
4. December 18, 96
Giant Foods
$64.75
Sixty-four and 75/100
food
Kristie Dando (signature)

Page 34

1. $132.50
2. $596.43
3. $453.21
4. $816.54

Page 35

5. $275.12
6. Barlow Florists
7. $25.50
8. flowers
9. $249.62
10. no
11. $249.62
12. $125.00
13. $374.62
14. car repairs
15. $45.72
16. no
17. $328.90
18. $875.26; $749.76
19. $749.76; $749.76; $717.61
20. $717.61; $717.61; $512.61

CONSUMER MATH

CONSUMER MATH 13

Page 37

$75.62
May 2, 1998
Atkins Lumber Co.
lumber
$525.15
$75.62
$449.53

—

May 2, 98
Atkins Lumber Co.
$75.62
Seventy-five and 62/100
lumber
Fran Wells

—

$48.16
May 4, 1998
Giant Foods
$449.53
$175.00
$624.53
$48.16
$576.37

—

May 4, 98
Giant Foods
$48.16
Forty-eight and 16/100
food
Fran Wells

—

$25.00
May 5, 1998
Dr. John Lavin
doctor's visit
$576.37
$25.00
$551.37

—

May 5, 98
Dr. John Lavin
$25.00
Twenty-five and no/100
doctor's visit
Fran Wells

Page 38

$68.75
September 2, 1997
Harris's Market
food
$728.32
$68.75

$659.57

—

September 2, 97
Harris's Market
$68.75
Sixty-eight and 75/100
food
Maria Chavez

—

$24.15
September 3, 1997
G & R Books
books
$659.57
$125.00
$784.57
$24.15
$760.42

—

September 3, 97
G & R Books
$24.15
Twenty-four and 15/100
books
Maria Chavez

Page 39

$210.00
September 6, 1997
Carroll Co. Bank
car payment
$760.42
$210.00
$550.42

—

September 6, 97
Carroll Co. Bank
$210.00
Two hundred ten and no/100
car payment
Maria Chavez

—

$165.25
September 10, 1997
Gas Company
utilities
$550.42
$450.00
$1,000.42
$165.25
$835.17

—

September 10, 97
Gas Company

$165.25
One hundred sixty-five and
    25/100
utilities
Maria Chavez

—

$78.65
September 11, 1997
Willis's Garage
car repair
$835.17
$78.65
$756.52

—

September 11, 97
Willis's Garage
$78.65
Seventy-eight and 65/100
car repair
Maria Chavez

Page 40

1. c	**6.** a
2. d	**7.** d
3. a	**8.** c
4. c	**9.** d
5. a	**10.** c

Page 41

1. 220	**10.** .00528
2. 196.08	**11.** .20748
3. 5.74	**12.** .014976
4. 73.5	**13.** 440
5. 1.415	**14.** 1,174.16
6. 77.4	**15.** 14.608
7. 94.22	**16.** 1.314
8. .12291	**17.** .0036
9. .135	**18.** .004272

Page 42

19. $294.00	**26.** $1,239.00
20. $1,438.40	**27.** $404.25
21. $652.50	**28.** $1,187.50
22. $149.50	**29.** $3,149.10
23. $679.50	**30.** $330.00
24. $373.00	**31.** $385.00
25 $353.40	**32.** $227.80

Page 43
1. $90
2. $90
3. $45
4. $30
5. $15

Page 44
6. $72
7. $28.80
8. $90
9. $18
10. $18
11. $36
12. $43.20
13. $54
14. $760
15. $874
16. $570
17. $76
18. $190
19. $304
20. $266
21. $532
22. $228

Page 45
1. $70
2. $30
3. $24
4. $15
5. $45
6. $41

Page 46
7. $702.50
8. $450
9. $380
10. $190
11. $300
12. $215
13. $63.25
14. $212.50
15. $119.25
16. $417.50
17. $4,000
18. $702.50
19. $450
20. $380
21. rent, transportation
22. May
23. April
24. $417.50
25. Answers may vary: clothing, entertainment, personal items

Page 47
1. 40%
2. 5%
3. 10%
4. 20%
5. 15%
6. 5%
7. 15%
8. 30%
9. 25%
10. 10%
11. 5%
12. 5%
13. clothing
14. transportation

Page 48
15. $22\frac{1}{2}$%
16. 15%
17. 10%
18. $6\frac{1}{4}$%
19. $6\frac{1}{4}$%
20. 5%
21. $4\frac{1}{2}$%
22. $5\frac{1}{2}$%
23. 5%
24. 20%
25. $33\frac{1}{3}$%
26. 20%
27. 5%
28. 10%
29. 4%
30. 8%
31. $1\frac{2}{3}$%
32. 6%
33. 10%
34. 2%
35. rent
36. rent
37. personal items
38. personal items
39. Ralph
40. $770.00
41. $300.00
42. $325.00

Page 49
1. 75
2. 128.6
3. 1.72
4. 720
5. 126.8
6. 836
7. 902.5
8. 1,260
9. 4,800
10. 76.3
11. 7,263
12. 75
13. 9,300
14. 274,000
15. 12,728.3
16. 8,230
17. 195
18. 129,720

Page 50
1. .45
2. .90
3. .04
4. .185
5. .25
6. .0775
7. .075
8. .1255
9. .085
10. .005
11. 72%
12. 12.5%
13. 65%
14. 11.25%
15. 5%
16. 37.5%
17. 6.5%
18. 8.2%
19. 4.5%
20. 12.65%

Page 52
1. $25.65; $1.28; $26.93
2. $67.80; $3.39; $71.19
3. $128.50; $5.14; $133.64
4. $73.50; $5.15; $78.65
5. $107.60; $6.46; $114.06
6. $32.65; $1.63; $34.28
7. $285.00; $11.40; $296.40
8. $187.50; $13.13; $200.63
9. $81.75; $3.27; $85.02
10. $228.00; $11.40; $239.40
11. $44.25; $1.77; $46.02
12. $79.90; $3.20; $83.10
13. $55.50; $2.78; $58.28

Page 53
1. $170.95
2. $803.21
3. $677.88
4. $892.27

Page 54
5. $83.04
6. $140.15
7. $470.55
8. $143.60
9. $1,777.00
10. $86.20
11. $3,450.18
12. $856.53
13. $1,087.52
14. $737.69
15. $600.90
16. $2,223.07
17. $711.90
18. $140.52
19. $3,001.48
20. $959.47

Page 56
1. $723.00; $148.00
2. $418.20; $43.20
3. $492.00; $77.00

4. $430.00; $50.00
5. $824.50; $74.50
6. $135.50; $10.50
7. $435.00; $50.00
8. $476.00; $51.00
9. $3,920.00; $420.00
10. $5,580.00; $580
11. $836.60; $71.60
12. $348.50; $53.50
13. $62.50; $562.50
14. $97.00; $388.00
15. $63.00; $252.00
16. $73.05; $413.95
17. $146.00; $584.00
18. $203.75; $611.25
19. $78.00; $572.00
20. $52.50; $122.50

Page 58
1. $2,131.20; $131.20
2. $1,971.00; $221.00
3. $675.00; $75.00
4. $2,949.30; $449.30
5. $1,976.40; $226.40
6. $4,902.00; $902.00
7. $955.20; $105.20
8. $5,395.00; $895.00
9. $4,500.00; $750.00
10. $6,240.60; $1,440.60
11. $4,083.90; $633.90
12. $3,133.80; $483.80
13. $1,340.00; $140.00
14. $7,410.00; $1,260.00
15. $963.60; $63.60
Calculator $192.50

Page 59
1. 12
2. 26
3. 63
4. 13.6
5. 2.04
6. 30
7. 4.5
8. 26.1
9. 3.5
10. 10
11. 9
12. 82
13. 32.4
14. 115.2
15. 7
16. 24
17. 27
18. 6

Page 60
1. 50
2. 75
3. 60
4. 20
5. 50
6. 25
7. 20
8. 40
9. 6
10. 25
11. 30
12. 31.25
13. 95
14. 30
15. 25
16. 50
17. 72
18. 2.5
19. 32
20. $53\frac{1}{3}$

Page 62
1. $15,844
2. $20,035
3. $17,700
4. $15,876
5. $13,510
6. $10,070
7. $12,840
8. $10,507
9. $11,190
10. $16,180
11. $10,035
12. $7,915
13. $11,800
14. $10,835
15. $16,335
16. $13,700

Page 63
1. $3,997.00
2. $2,682.20
3. $4,310.05
4. $3,975.45

Page 64
5. $200.00; $4,242.50
6. $70.00; $1,851.00
7. $325.00; $6,881.75
8. $349.65; $5,387.15
9. $519.00; $9,212.50
10. $151.00; $3,959.50
11. $125.00; $2,664.50
12. $314.00; $8,218.00
13. $570.00; $10,144.00
14. $87.50; $1,368.00
15. $239.80; $6,270.30
16. $630.00; $13,318.50
17. $461.70; $8,197.70
18. $4,876.50
19. $6,907.50
20. $5,157.50
Calculator $3,900

Page 65
1. $2,100
2. $4,125
3. $2,450

Page 66
4. $12,325
5. $14,900
6. $1,740; $7,938; $9,678
7. $925; $9,824; $10,749
8. $1,575; $10,263.60; $11,838.60
9. $1,380; $6,072; $7,452
10. $3,087.50; $11,114.40; $14,201.90
11. $950; $9,833.40; $10,783.40
12. $862.50; $5,620; $6,482.50
13. $2,240; $10,800; $13,040
14. $1,764; $9,241.20; $11,005.20
15. $1,275; $7,736; $9,011
16. $2,400; $8,265.60; $10,665.60
17. $580; $5,700; $6,280
18. $4,680; $11,520; $16,200
Calculator $664

Page 67
1. $385.15
2. $457.85
3. $432.10
4. $451.45

Page 68
5. $102.00; $323.35
6. $110.75; $302.20
7. $112.85; $318.85
8. $105.50; $320.10
9. $131.65; $369.70
10. $145.95; $384.20
11. $99.50; $301.90
12. $120.40; $369.70
13. $105.50; $298.50
14. $112.85; $350.25
15. $321.50
16. $216.22
Calculator $250; $437.50; $562.50

Page 69
1. $2,400
2. $3,840
3. $5,040

4. $5,920
5. $6,720

Page 70
6. $8,806
7. $6,541.60
8. $4,654.60
9. $3,270.80
10. $2,012.80
11. 63%; $13,230; $7,770
12. 74%; $18,500; $6,500
13. 48%; $6,000; $6,500
14. 84%; $18,900; $3,600
15. 48%; $4,560; $4,940
16. 30%; $7,050; $16,450
17. 63%; $11,025; $6,475
18. 74%; $6,845; $2,405
19. 84%; $19,194; $3,656
20. 30%; $2,295; $5,355
21. 48%; $5,520; $5,980
22. 74%; $23,680; $8,320
23. 84%; $20,664; $3,936
24. 63%; $11,907; $6,993
25. 48%; $4,320; $4,680

Page 71
1. $.33
2. $.51
3. $.38
4. $.42

Page 72
5. $75.24
6. $58.91
7. $49.38
8. $2,800; $.28
9. $3,000; $.25
10. $2,500; $.31
11. $2,000; $.16
12. $1,850; $.20
13. $2,310; $.23
14. $1,960; $.16
15. $2,500; $.17

Page 73
1. d
2. a
3. b
4. c
5. b
6. d
7. d
8. a
9. c
10. b

Page 74
1. $\frac{1}{2}$
2. $\frac{2}{3}$
3. $\frac{2}{3}$
4. $\frac{4}{5}$
5. $\frac{1}{2}$
6. $\frac{3}{4}$
7. $\frac{1}{4}$
8. $\frac{5}{6}$
9. $\frac{7}{8}$
10. $\frac{3}{4}$
11. $\frac{3}{5}$
12. $\frac{1}{4}$
13. $\frac{1}{5}$
14. $\frac{3}{4}$
15. $\frac{5}{8}$
16. $\frac{1}{2}$
17. $\frac{1}{4}$
18. $\frac{18}{25}$
19. $\frac{3}{4}$
20. $\frac{2}{3}$
21. $\frac{1}{3}$
22. $\frac{7}{12}$
23. $\frac{2}{5}$
24. $\frac{1}{5}$
25. $\frac{6}{7}$
26. $\frac{1}{4}$
27. $\frac{1}{3}$
28. $\frac{9}{25}$
29. $\frac{4}{5}$
30. $\frac{1}{2}$

Page 75
1. 50%
2. 75%
3. $62\frac{1}{2}$%
4. $66\frac{2}{3}$%
5. 60%
6. 90%
7. 5%
8. 68%
9. $33\frac{1}{3}$%
10. $87\frac{1}{2}$%
11. $7\frac{1}{2}$%
12. 30%
13. 95%
14. 18%
15. $83\frac{1}{3}$%
16. $37\frac{1}{2}$%
17. 28%
18. $31\frac{1}{4}$%
19. $12\frac{1}{2}$%
20. $16\frac{2}{3}$%
21. 70%
22. $33\frac{1}{3}$%
23. 45%
24. 64%
25. 70%

Page 77
1. $.04
2. $.15
3. $.59
4. $1.14
5. $.09
6. $.65
7. $1.14; $20.09
8. $.66; $11.61
9. $.09; $1.58
10. $.72; $12.71
11. $32.50; $682.50
12. $1.20; $21.15
13. $1.65; $29.15
14. $5.00; $130.00
15. $.44; $11.39
16. $10.75; $225.75
17. $2.00; $30.50
18. $266.70; $4,711.70
19. $2.63; $46.38
20. $.84; $17.64
Calculator $30.10

Page 78
1. 40
2. 250
3. 780
4. 658
5. 1,250
6. 1,045
7. 909
8. 2,500
9. 821
10. 154
11. 470
12. 870
13. 2,255
14. 329
15. 286
16. 747
17. 109
18. 1,011

Page 79
19. $25,500
20. $66,825
21. $66,360
22. $57,000
23. $10,725
24. $6,061
25. $2,550
26. $3,751.78
27. $9,375; $421.88
28. $66,600; $3,496.50
29. $36,000; $1,710
30. $137,500; $5,500
31. $41,100; $2,527.65
32. $40,040; $2,262.26
33. $65,000; $2,730
34. $42,500; $2,656.25
35. $50,000; $3,750
36. $103,500; $6,986.25
37. $18,600; $651
38. $52,800; $2,640
Calculator $120,000

Page 80
1. $15,155.34
2. $1,756
3. $564.35
4. $1,083.60

Page 81
5. $17,900
6. $26,930
7. $19,544
8. $13,959
9. $30,350
10. $28,185
11. $31,230
12. $27,750

Page 82
1. $14,305
2. $19,370
3. $16,385
4. $71,455

Page 83
5. $5,000; $17,449
6. $2,500; $10,387
7. $7,500; $19,512
8. $10,000; $23,075
9. $7,500; $16,675
10. $12,500; $21,700
11. $5,000; $6,115
12. $10,000; $42,055
13. $15,000; $52,305
14. $7,500; $23,275
15. $10,000; $98,029
16. $34,015
17. $26,580
18. $50,570
Calculator $6,080

Page 84
1. $1\frac{1}{4}$
2. 1
3. $\frac{7}{8}$
4. $1\frac{1}{6}$
5. $1\frac{1}{10}$
6. $1\frac{1}{5}$

Page 85
7. $\frac{7}{8}$
8. $1\frac{1}{2}$
9. $1\frac{3}{8}$
10. $1\frac{2}{5}$
11. $1\frac{5}{8}$
12. $1\frac{1}{12}$
13. $\frac{11}{24}$
14. $1\frac{23}{40}$
15. $\frac{19}{24}$
16. $\frac{1}{4}$
17. $\frac{1}{4}$
18. $\frac{1}{8}$
19. $\frac{1}{8}$
20. $\frac{1}{2}$
21. $\frac{1}{12}$
22. $\frac{1}{3}$
23. $\frac{5}{12}$
24. $\frac{3}{10}$
25. $\frac{1}{6}$
26. $\frac{1}{3}$
27. $\frac{1}{6}$
28. $\frac{1}{16}$
29. $\frac{1}{16}$
30. $\frac{3}{16}$
31. $1\frac{1}{4}$ hours
32. $\frac{1}{8}$ hour

Page 87
1. $1,183.81
2. $2,646.19
3. $16,159.89
4. $6,505.82
5. 1.271224; $635.61; $135.61
6. 1.476930; $1,476.93; $476.93

7. 1.014278; $1,521.42; $21.42
8. 1.083278; $2,166.56; $166.56
9. 1.822006; $9,110.03; $4,110.03
10. 1.169103; $2,922.76; $422.76
11. 1.283998; $1,284.00; $284.00
12. 1.019291; $4,077.16; $77.16
13. 1.568240; $3,136.48; $1,136.48
14. 1.785936; $2,678.90; $1,178.90
15. 1.221376; $6,106.88; $1,106.88
16. 1.075185; $6,451.11; $451.11

Page 89
1. $25
2. $37.50
3. $100
4. $250
5. $5000
6. $90.84
7. $170.72
8. $361.20
9. $784.80
10. $75; $28.14; $84.42; $9.42
11. $100; $36.12; $144.48; $44.48
12. $50; $39.24; $78.48; $28.48
13. $250; $32.92; $329.20; $79.20
14. $50; $46.46; $92.92; $42.92
15. $500; $30.28; $605.60; $105.60
16. $2,500; $36.12; $3,612; $1,112
17. $25; $42.68; $42.68; $17.68
18. $5,000; $39.24; $7,848; $2,848

Page 91
1. $2,750
2. $35,500
3. $9,062.50
4. $3,287.50
5. $30\frac{1}{2}$; $3,050; $3,085.75
6. 8; $1,600; $1,650.15
7. $30\frac{1}{8}$; $4,518.75; $4,563.95
8. $20\frac{1}{4}$; $8,100; $8,172.50
9. $39\frac{5}{8}$; $9,906.25; $9,967.10

10. $7\frac{3}{8}$; $7,375; $7,495.80
11. $44\frac{3}{4}$; $26,850; $26,935.75
12. $31\frac{1}{4}$; $15,625; $15,700.95
13. $14\frac{3}{4}$; $14,750; $14,875.75
14. $43\frac{1}{4}$; $25,950; $26,032.50
15. $21\frac{3}{4}$; $43,500; $43,700.00

Page 92
1. $127
2. $467.50
3. $1,314.00
4. $500.50

Page 93
5. 6%
6. 5%
7. 8%
8. $7\frac{1}{2}$%
9. $51.00; 4%
10. $232; 8%
11. $165.75; 5%
12. $371.25; $7\frac{1}{2}$%
13. $780.00; 6%
14. $1,000; 10%
15 $3,420; 8%
16. $539.00; $3\frac{1}{2}$%
17. $335.50; $11\frac{1}{4}$%
18. $1,125.60; 5%
19. $762.20; 5%
20. $101.65; 3%

Page 94
1. d
2. a
3. c
4. b
5. d
6. b
7. b
8. a
9. c
10. a

Pages 95–96
1. d
2. a
3. c
4. c
5. d
6. d
7. d
8. a
9. a
10. b
11. c
12. b
13. d
14. c
15. a
16. b
17. c
18. c
19. d
20. a

Learning to Budget

Pages 8–9
Answers may vary, but Joey could spend less money for such items as lunches, gifts, clothes, and miscellaneous expenses.

Page 10
1. budget
2. Inflation
3. money manager
4. budget record form
5. Estimated income
6. money management
7. Estimated expenses
8. gross earnings
9. h   **13.** e
10. g   **14.** a
11. d   **15.** f
12. b   **16.** c

Page 11
17. *Inflation* means that values are lower and prices have risen. As a result, an item costs more now than it did last year.
18. *Money management* means handling your income wisely by planning how it will be spent.
19. A *money manager* is a person who handles his or her money wisely.
20. A *budget* is a plan for spending income.
21. *Estimated income* is the amount of money that a person expects to receive during the budget period.
22. *Estimated expenses* are items or services that a person plans to buy with income during the budget period.
23. A *budget record form* is used to write down plans for spending money.
24. *Net earnings* are the actual cash a person has to spend after deductions.

Page 18
1. Cash on hand $12.10
   Estimated income $285.87
2. Total estimated cash $297.97
3. Estimated expenses
   Savings $25.00
   Room and board $50.00
   Lunches $40.00
   Bus fare $40.00
   Vacation fund $20.00

Medical expenses $25.00
Entertainment $20.00
Gift fund $9.50
Grooming needs $10.00
Clothing fund $20.00
Misc. expenses $25.00
4. Total expenses $284.50
5. $297.97
6. $284.50
7. $13.47
8. Write $13.47 on the form.

Page 19
Budget record form should be filled in correctly. Figures should match those listed for page 18.

Page 20
1. The Clarks are spending too much money.
2. Six (2 credit cards, rent payment, car payment, and 2 store charge account payments)
3. The Clarks have too many expensive items on their wants list. They should cut back on credit spending. They want to buy too many new items, which will get them more in debt.
4. The Clarks should revise the needs and wants list. They should cut back on their credit spending. They should not buy any new items until they pay off their present bills.

Page 21
5. Suggested answers could include:

Cash on hand	$0.00
Salary	$875.28
Total cash	$875.28

Expenses:

Rent	$350.00
Food	$200.00
Car payment	$104.12
Charge account payment	$50.00
Charge account payment	$50.00
Credit card payment	$50.00
Credit card payment	$50.00
Down payment for house	$11.00
Total cash	$875.28
Total expenses	$865.12
Cash on hand	$10.16

Page 22
1. Needs   Wants
   a. Rent   f. New leather coat
   b. Groceries   g. New motorcycle
   c. Medical bills   h. Entertainment
   d. Credit card   i. Stereo for car
   e. Utility bills   j. Concert ticket
2. Rick has too many expenses. He should not buy a leather coat or a motorcycle until he pays off his bills.
3. Rick is making several credit card payments. He wants to buy a motorcycle and a leather coat—things that will need more credit. He has too many bills. He needs to pay off money he owes before getting into more debt.
4. He should revise his needs and wants list. He should make fewer credit card purchases. He should cut back on entertainment expenses.

Page 23
5. Suggested answers could include:

Rent	$300.00	Cash on hand	$596.32
Groceries	$150.00	Salary	$590.00
Medical bills	$20.00	Total cash	$6.32
Credit card	$50.00		
Utility bill	$40.00		
Concert ticket	$20.00		
Entertainment	$10.00		
Total expenses	$590.00		

Page 25
1. Needs   Wants
   a. Rent   f. Television
   b. Phone bill   g. Concert tickets
   c. Medical bills   h. New kitchen appliances
   d. Charge acct.   i. New sofa
      payment   j. New car
   e. Groceries
2. They need to rethink their needs and wants. They have too many bills to pay.
3. They are confusing needs and wants. They need to charge fewer items. They need to decide what wants are most important.
4. They could pay off credit payments before charging new items. They could buy one or two new items, not four.

Pages 26–27

1. No
2. Needs

   a. Food
   b. Mortgage payment
   c. Utility bills
   d. Two car payments
   e. Doctor's bills
   f. Money owed to friends
   g. Credit card payment
   h. Video camera payment

   Wants

   i. Television
   j. Washing machine
   k. Concert tickets
   l. Living room furniture
   m. Third car

3. Dave and Lois have too many bills. They need to rethink their needs and wants.
4. They are confusing their needs and wants. They have bills to pay off. They are making too many credit card purchases. If they have to borrow money from friends, they are spending too much.
5. They should revise their needs and wants list. They should cut back on their credit spending. They should go to a movie instead of a concert. They could spend less on entertainment. They could cut down on their driving. They should not buy dining room furniture or a television until they pay off old bills.

Page 28

6. Answers will vary. Possible answers:

Cash on hand	$0.00
Salary	$3,285.76
Total cash	$3,285.76
Food	$525.00
Mortgage	$995.00
Utility	$85.00
Two car payments	$565.00
Doctor's bills	$75.00
Money owed to friends	$85.00
Credit card payment	$275.00
Video camera payment	$35.00
Total cash	$3,285.76
Total expenses	$2,640.00
Cash on hand	$645.76

They can apply cash on hand to their debt.

Pages 29–30

Answers will vary.

Page 31

1. Needs
2. Spending habits
3. net income
4. Decision making
5. Values
6. Goals
7. Wants
8. f
9. d
10. e
11. g
12. b
13. a
14. c

Answers will vary for items 15–18 but could include:

15. Goal: Finishing school, getting a job, buying a car
16. Value: Honesty, hard work, family
17. Decision making: Choosing to go to college or to rent an apartment or to work at a certain job
18. Need: Food, clothing, housing, medical care

Page 32

1. money manager, budget
2. Inflation
3. needs
4. values
5. gross
6. net
7. N
8. W
9. N
10. N
11. N
12. N
13. N
14. W
15. a. $452.17
    b. $425.00
    c. $27.17

Page 33

A. See Budget Record Form answers for page 34.

B.
3. $310.49
4. $304.50
5. $5.99

Page 34

Estimated expenses:

Savings	$25.00	Cash on hand	$14.92
Room and board	$50.00	Salary	$295.57
Lunches	$40.00	Total cash	$310.49
Bus fare	$40.00		
Vacation fund	$20.00		
Gift fund	$9.50		
Eye exam	$35.00		
Grooming needs	$15.00		
Clothing fund	$30.00		
Contributions	$15.00		
Misc. expenses	$25.00		
Total cash	$310.49		
Total expenses	$304.50		
Cash on hand	$5.99		

Page 35

A. See Budget Record Form answers for page 36.

B.
3. $312.00
4. $269.50
5. Yes
6. $42.50
7. Cash on hand
8. As cash on hand on top line

Page 36

Estimated expenses:

Savings	$25.00	Cash on hand	$16.13
Room and board	$50.00	Salary	$295.87
Lunches	$40.00	Total cash	$312.00
Vacation fund	$20.00		
Gift fund	$9.50		
Dental exam	$40.00		
Grooming needs	$10.00		
Clothing fund	$35.00		
Doctor bill	$15.00		
Misc. expenses	$25.00		
Total cash	$312.00		
Total expenses	$269.50		
Cash on hand	$42.50		

Pages 37–38

1. No

   Needs

   a. Car payment
   b. Groceries
   c. Rent
   d. Credit payment
   e. Car repair bill
   f. Eye exam payment

   Wants

   g. New motorcycle
   h. Vacation
   i. Motorcycle repair
   j. New CD player

2. Sam has many expenses. He needs to examine his needs and wants list.
3. Sam is confusing many items on his needs and wants list.

He owes money on credit purchases and on his car. He wants to buy new want items, which will get him more in debt.

4. Sam should revise his needs and wants list. He should cut back on his credit spending. He should not take a vacation until he gets out of debt.

5. Suggested answers include:

Car payment	$100.00
Eye exam bill	$30.00
Groceries	$60.00
New motorcycle	$10.00
Rent	$150.00
Vacation	$10.00
Credit payment	$20.00
Motorcycle repair	$25.00
Car repair bill	$20.00
New CD player	$10.00
Total cash	$497.00
Total expenses	$435.00
Cash on hand	$62.00

Page 39

1. Needs
   a. Room and board
   b. Bus fare for work
   c. Dentist bill
   d. Pay back loan to her mother
   e. Car repair bill

   Wants
   f. New party dress
   g. New ring
   h. Money for beauty shop
   i. Tickets for play
   j. Lunches at work

2. Rita has many bills to pay off. She needs to revise her needs and wants list.

3. Rita confuses many of her needs and wants. She has many bills to pay off. She wants to buy new want items, which will get her more in debt.

4. Rita should revise her needs and wants list. She should not buy any new want items until she pays off her bills. She should style her hair so that she can care for it herself.

Page 40

5. Suggested answers include:

Car repair bill	$40.00	Cash on hand	$0.00
Room and board	$180.00	Salary	$484.00
Bus fare	$20.00	Total cash	$484.00
Dentist bill	$20.00		
Loan from mother	$20.00		
Party dress	$20.00		
New ring	$40.00		

Lunches at work	$50.00
Beauty shop	$40.00
Tickets for play	$40.00
Total cash	$484.00
Total expenses	$470.00
Cash on hand	$14.00

Page 41

A. See Budget Record Form answers for page 42.

B.
1. $174.78
2. $170.00
3. $4.78
4. $154.78

Page 42

Estimated expenses:

Room and board	$50.00	Cash on hand	$20.00
Savings	$20.00	Salary	$154.78
Clothes	$30.00	Total cash	$174.78
Entertainment	$25.00		
Grooming needs	$10.00		
Bus fare	$20.00		
Miscellaneous items	$15.00		
Total cash	$174.78		
Total expenses	$170.00		
Cash on hand	$4.78		

Page 43

A. See Budget Record Form answers for page 44.

B.
1. $358.26
2. $354.46
3. $3.80
4. $336.48

Page 44

Estimated expenses:

Rent	$70.00	Cash on hand	$21.78
Motorcycle pymt	$154.46	Salary	$336.48
Savings	$20.00	Total cash	$358.26
Lunches	$20.00		
Entertainment	$35.00		
Motorcycle exp.	$40.00		
Personal needs	$5.00		
Miscellaneous	$10.00		
Total cash	$358.26		
Total expenses	$354.46		
Cash on hand	$3.80		

Page 45

A. See Budget Record Form answers for page 46.

B.
1. $1,115.51
2. $1,087.00
3. $28.51
4. $1,090.51

Page 46

Estimated expenses:

Mortgage payment	$375.00	Cash on hand	$25.00
Furniture payment	$142.00	Salary	$1,090.51
Savings	$20.00	Total cash	$1,115.51
Utility bills	$100.00		
Credit card payment	$175.00		
Groceries	$150.00		
Children's allowance	$40.00		
Grooming needs	$15.00		
Entertainment	$40.00		
Miscellaneous items	$30.00		
Total cash	$1,115.51		
Total expenses	$1,087.00		
Cash on hand	$28.51		

Page 50

1. $92.16
2. $107.52
3. $38.40
4. $61.44
5. $69.12
6. $76.80
7. $30.72
8. $23.04
9. $84.48
10. $53.76

Page 51

1. $316.80
2. $95.04
3. $110.88
4. $253.44
5. $158.40
6. $158.40
7. $142.56

Page 52

1. $451.20
2. $112.80
3. $270.72
4. $225.60
5. $496.32
6. $135.36

Page 54

1. $520.00
2. $1,300.00
3. $442.00
4. $494.00
5. $390.00

LEARNING TO BUDGET

Page 55
1. $468.00
2. $338.00
3. $900.00
4. $416.00
5. $442.00
6. $884.00
7. $540.10
8. $49.00
9. $90.50
10. $470.00, $131.60, $376, $263.20

Page 56
2. $329.27
3. $321.00
4. $8.27
5. $142.00
6. $177.50
7. $159.75
8. $88.75
9. $88.75
10. $319.50
11. $213.00
12. $248.50
13. $284.00
14. $53.25

Page 64

Date	Explanation	Expense	Balance
5/17	Savings account	$30.00	$224.63
5/17	Vacation	$20.00	$204.63
5/18	Lunches	$20.00	$184.63
5/18	Bus fare	$20.00	$164.63
5/18	Gift fund	$9.50	$155.13
5/18	Stereo fund	$2.00	$153.13
5/19	Medical fund	$15.00	$138.13

Page 67
1. Complete balance column. Draw a red line under the last entry.
2. Write temporary totals.
3.
a. $12.10
b. $295.57
c. $307.67
d. $294.36
e. $13.31
4. Yes
5. Write the word *totals*. Write the total and final balance figures in ink.
6. Close the cash record. Draw a line under the totals.

Page 68
Line Balance
8. $212.67
9. $208.67
10. $188.67
11. $168.67
12. $133.67
13. $125.17
14. $113.71
15. $101.21
16. $90.71
17. $86.71
18. $56.83
19. $36.83
20. $16.83
21. $13.31
22. Total income $307.67
Total expenses $294.36
Balance $13.31

Page 69
1. Complete the balance column. Draw a red line under the last entry.
2. Write the temporary totals.
3.
a. $13.31
b. $295.57
c. $308.88
d. $290.51
e. $18.37
4. Yes
5. Write the word *totals* and final balance figures in ink.
6. Close the cash record. Draw a line under the totals.

Page 70
Line Balance
8. $213.88
9. $193.88
10. $173.88
11. $162.38
12. $155.88
13. $130.88
14. $118.88
15. $88.88
16. $83.63
17. $75.63
18. $73.63
19. $53.63
20. $33.63
21. $28.87
22. $18.37
23. Total income $308.88
Total expenses $290.51
Balance $18.37

Page 71
1. budget
2. Cash on hand
3. Cash record
4. Cash/income column
5. Explanation column
6. Expense column
7. Balance column
8. b
9. c
10. e
11. g
12. a
13. d
14. f

Page 72
15. A *budget* is a plan that shows how a person will spend income during the budget period.
16. A *cash record* is a form that shows how money was spent during the budget period.
17. The *explanation column* is the place on the cash record that describes how money was received or spent.
18. The *income column* shows the amount of money that was received during the budget period.
19. The *expense column* shows the amount of money spent during the budget period.
20. The *balance column* shows the cash on hand after money is received or spent.
21. *Cash on hand* is the amount of money that a person has at the beginning and end of the budget period.

Page 73
1. salary
2. Cash on hand
3. Inflation
4. Expenses
5. Wants
6. budget
7. Values
8. Fixed expenses
9. Needs
10. cash record
11. Variable expenses
12. Decision making
13. Temporary totals
14. income

15. manage
16. balance

Page 74

17. c	**28.** k
18. j	**29.** income
19. a	**30.** record
20. f	**31.** budget
21. h	**32.** expenses
22. i	**33.** inflation
23. b	**34.** balance
24. e	**35.** estimated
25. d	**36.** temporary
26. g	**37.** money
27. l	**38.** values

Page 75

```
R E C O R D  H S A  C
T E M P O R A R Y  E
E A B N E E D S P  S
X R E I N C O M E  T
P N C P T U V S R  I
E I A X L D U I I  M
N N L Y M A Y L O  A
S G L Z P D N A D  T
E  S A L A R Y T O C E
S B B U D G E T D  E
```

Page 76

39. *Inflation* is caused by a decrease in value and a rise in prices. It causes items to cost more this year than they did last year.
40. Houses, clothing, shoes, and appliances are examples of items that cost more now than they did.
41. One could deal with inflation by learning new skills to find a higher-paying job, by getting a raise to provide more money, or by comparison shopping to find the best prices. One can also make decisions about what items should be purchased and whether they are worth the higher price.
42. A *budget* is a plan for spending estimated income.
43. A *cash record* is an itemized list of income and expenses.
44. *Needs* are items that people need to survive.
45. *Wants* are items that people like but can do without.

46. Needs are more important than wants because they are necessary for survival.
47. Budget *goals* help people decide which needs and wants are more important. They help people plan where money will be spent.
48. *Values* describe how people feel about things. They are standards of importance or desirability.
49. People spend money on the things that they value most.
50. One must decide which needs or wants are important.
51. To balance a budget, one checks to see that the final balance equals the total income minus total expenses.
52. If a budget does not balance, one can check for errors in math and correct them. One can also spend less in the next budget period to make up for earlier overspending.
53. The balance column tells cash on hand on a given date.

Page 77
A. See Budget Record Form answers for page 78.
B.
1. $615.52
2. $20.75
3. $636.27
4. $485.00
5. $625.00
6. $11.27

Page 78
Estimated expenses:

Rent	$295.00	Cash on hand	$20.75
Insurance	$50.00	Salary	$615.52
Car expenses	$40.00	Total cash	$636.27
Food	$150.00		
Vacation fund	$20.00		
Medical expenses	$10.00		
Utility bills	$40.00		
Misc. expenses	$20.00		
Total cash	$636.27		
Total expenses	$625.00		
Cash on hand	$11.27		

Page 80
Line Balance

7. $321.27	**14.** $137.95
8. $278.41	**15.** $127.95
9. $238.69	**16.** $121.20
10. $222.69	**17.** $104.42
11. $212.69	**18.** $94.42
12. $193.19	**19.** $44.42
13. $178.19	**20.** $4.42

Page 81
1. Add the temporary totals.
2.
a. $20.75
b. $615.52
c. $636.27
d. $631.85
e. $4.42
3. Yes
4. Draw the red line under the totals.

Page 82
1. $636.27
2. $636.27
3. No difference
4. $625.00
5. $631.85
6. A difference of $6.85. Actual expenses were higher.
7. Yes; he spent more money than he estimated, but his total expenses were still less than his total income.

Page 83
A. See Budget Record Form answers for page 84.
B.
1. $466.93
2. $457.00
3. $9.93

Page 84
Estimated expenses:

Room and board	$100.00
Savings	$15.00
Transportation	$40.00
Clothing	$60.00
Dental work	$70.00
Entertainment	$30.00
Vacation fund	$12.00
Medical expenses	$50.00
Lunches	$20.00
Insurance	$30.00
Miscellaneous	$30.00
Cash on hand	$12.50
Estimated income	$454.43
Total cash	$466.93

Total expenses $457.00
Cash on hand $9.93

Page 86

Line	Balance	Line	Balance
4.	$12.50	14.	$218.35
5.	$466.93	15.	$198.35
6.	$451.93	16.	$162.35
7.	$351.93	17.	$157.79
8.	$337.33	18.	$128.03
9.	$317.33	19.	$123.78
10.	$305.33	20.	$53.78
11.	$255.33	21.	$23.78
12.	$248.33	22.	$10.83
13.	$238.35		

Page 87
1. Cash/Income $466.93
   Total expenses $456.10
2.
   a. $12.50
   b. $454.43
   c. $466.93
   d. $456.10
   e. $10.83
3. Yes
4. Draw a double-ruled line.

Page 88
1. $466.93
2. $466.93
3. No difference
4. $457.00
5. $456.10
6. $.90 difference. Estimated expenses were higher.
7. Yes; her total expenses were less than her total income.

Page 89
A. Answers will vary. See page 90.
B.
1. $298.24
2. Rent $75.00; other expenses can vary but must include lunches and bus fare.
3. Answers will vary.

Page 90
Complete budget form correctly. Actual figures will vary.

Page 91
1. Complete cash record correctly.
2. Figure temporary totals
3.
a. $3.25   d. Answers will vary.

b. $298.24   e. Answers will vary.
c. $301.49
4. Yes
5. Add the word *totals*, write totals in ink, and draw double line.

Page 92
Complete cash record form correctly. Actual figures will vary.

Page 93
1. $301.49
2. $301.49
3. No difference
4–6. Answers will vary.
7. Student lives within budget if total income is more than or equal to total expenses.

Page 94
1. needs
2. budget
3. cash on hand
4. fixed expenses
5. wants
6. salary
7. values
8. balance
9. inflation
10. cash record
11. happens when a person considers all possible choices when solving a problem
12. figures written in pencil
13. expenses not occurring regularly in a budget
14. how a person chooses to buy things
15. things that one hopes to accomplish
16. the total amount of money that a person earns
17. the amount of money that a person is left with after certain deductions (i.e., taxes)
18. describes how money was received or spent in the cash record
19. shows cash on hand after money is received or spent
20. a form that shows how money was spent during a budget period

Page 95
1.

a.	N	f.	N
b.	W	g.	N
c.	W	h.	N
d.	W	i.	W
e.	N	j.	N

2. Joe has too many expenses. He should limit his wants. He should not purchase any new items until he has paid off his credit card debt.
3.
a. decrease his wants list
b. make fewer credit card purchases
c. spend less on entertainment and vacations
4. $362.47
5. $384.32
6. $350.00
7. $34.32

Page 96

Line 4	Cash/Income	$21.85
Line 5	Cash/Income	$362.47
Line 5	Balance	$384.32
Line 6	Expense	$354.32
Line 7	Expense	$339.32
Line 8	Expense	$234.32
Line 9	Expense	$194.32
Line 10	Expense	$114.32
Line 11	Expense	$94.32
Line 12	Expense	$34.32

Practical Math

Page 5
1. 52.01
2. 55.26
3. 522.57
4. 1.652
5. 62.0245
6. 36.373
7. 14.546
8. 365.65
9. 783.175
10. 89.858
11. 1.068
12. 25.319
13. 11.75
14. 0.8996
15. 10.049
16. 30.05
17. 2.9776
18. 1.925
19. 13.817
20. 0.911

Page 6
1. $350
2. $135
3. $75
4. $117

Page 7
5. $44
6. $80
7. $22.50
8. $240
9. $146.25
10. $900
11. $45
12. $567
13. $2,475
14. $63
15. $320
16. $149.50
17. $300

Page 8
1. $100; 2,100; 105.00; 2,205.00; 110.25; 2,315.25
2. $40; 540; 43.20; 583.20; 46.66; 629.86
3. $240; 4,240; 254.40; 4,494.40l; 269.66; 4,764.06
4. $120; 1,620; 129.60; 1,749.60; 139.97; 1,889.57
5. $225; 2,725; 245.25 2,970.25; 267.32; 3,237.57
6. $210; 3,210; 224.70; 3,434.70; 240.43; 3,675.13
7. $750; 10,750; 806.25; 11,556.25; 866.72; 12,422.97

Page 9
8. $1,685.40
9. $4,831.80
10. $1,048.63
11. $9,550.63
12. $2,024.76
13. $3,716.48
14. $4,350.20
15 $3,288.21
16. $1,632.58

Page 11
1. 1.2625
2. 2.1589
3. 1.6058
4. 3.2071
5. 1.4258
6. 1.4775
7. 1.1475; $2,295.00
8. 1.3382; $669.10
9. 1.2250; $1,837.50
10. 1.4775; $5,910.00
11. 1.5869; $1,269.52
12. 1.5513; $11,634.75
13. 1.7908; $2,148.96
14. 1.3449; $8,069.40
15. 1.9990; $1,299.35
16. 2.0122; $20,122.00
17. 1.3159; $3,947.70
18. 12
19. 9
20. 19

Page 12
1. $75
2. $528
3. $236.05
4. $1,605.35
5. $682.50
6. $3,325.93
7. $1,543.60
8. $1,065.50

Page 13
9. $1,325.70
10. $937.53
11. $1,132.73
12. $1,247.73
13. $1,172.73
14. $1,350.94
15. $1,101.06
16. $976.06
17. $1,133.06
18. $1,225.67
19. $1,425.23
20. $1,548.16

Page 15
1.
Dateline:
December 20, (current year)
Pay to the Order of:
Civil War Times
Check amount: $18.95
Eighteen and 95/100—
Memo: subscription
Signature: Wilmer Jones
2.
Date line:
December 20, (current year)
Pay to the Order of:
Mary's Dress Shop
Check amount: $75.00
Seventy-five and no/100—
Memo: dress
Signature: Mary Jane Harris

Page 16
3.
Date line: June 12, (current year)
Pay to the Order of:
Fast Food Store
Check amount: $27.95
Twenty-seven and 95/100—
Memo: groceries
Signature: Christa Woods
4.
Date line: July 25, (current year)
Pay to the Order of:
Green Machine
Check amount: $85.50
Eighty-five and 50/100—
Memo: lawn care
Signature: Jim Cansey

Page 17
1. 68
2. 137.2
3. 1.89
4. 690
5. .73
6. 935
7. 807.2
8. 1,350
9. 6,200
10. 2.8
11. 4,675
12. 98
13. 4,700
14. 183,000
15. 13,607.5
16. 94,700
17. 830
18. .732

Page 18
1.
a. $173.91
b. $258.91
c. $213.76
d. $153.61

Page 19
2.
a. $617.50
b. $792.50
c. $767.55
d. $672.43
e. $847.43
3.
a. 7/25; deposit; $150.00; $858.12
b. 8/2; Finer Foods; $65.18; $792.94
c. 8/3; Kelly's Meats; $125.00; $667.94
d. 8/5; Provident Sav. Bank; $187.50; $480.44

e. 8/6; Thomas Bann; $20.00; $460.44

f. 8/7; deposit; $150.00; $610.44

g. 8/8; W. Ball & Co.; $29.95; $580.49

h. 8/10; Bill's Hardware; $48.16; $532.33

Page 20

1. 8	**8.** 13.6
2. 25	**9.** .63
3. 32	**10.** 4.77
4. 9	**11.** .07
5. .7	**12.** 27.00
6. 3.7	**13.** $1.30
7. .1	

Page 21

1. .28	**11.** 65%
2. .80	**12.** 16.5%
3. .03	**13.** 8%
4. .125	**14.** 11.75%
5. .9862	**15.** 7.2%
6. .0525	**16.** $62\frac{1}{2}$%
7. .095	**17.** $8\frac{1}{4}$%
8. .126781	**18.** 9.3%
9. .025	**19.** 34%
10. .004	**20.** 24%

Page 23

1. $129.60
2. $297.00
3. $378.00
4. $148.50
5. $280.80
6. $475.20
7. $212.00; $15.90; $227.90
8. $196.20; $49.05; $245.25
9. $244.00; $73.20; $317.20
10. $199.50; $39.38; $238.88
11. $246.00; $110.70; $356.70
12. $294.00; $88.20; $382.20
13. $244.80; $102.00; $346.80
14. $288.00; $129.60; $417.60
15. $260.00; $195.00; $455.00
16. $154.50; $77.25; $231.75
17. $494.00
18. $350.50
19. $510.63
20. $627.00

Page 25

1. $45.00
2. $160.00
3. $60.00
4. $120.00

5. $117.00
6. $112.50
7. $25.20
8. $390.00
9. $562.50
10. $220; $30; $250
11. $270; $100; $370
12. $254; $102; $356
13. $288; $44; $332
14. $200; $50; $250
15. $260; $135; $395
16. $350; $125; $475
17. $204; $140; $344
18. $225; $90; $315
19. $504; $126; $630
20. $285; $192; $477

Page 26

1. $146.20
2. $157.67

Page 27

3. $234;00; $185.50
4. $290.00; $217.85
5. $199.50; $161.38
6. $185.40; $143.10
7. $368.00; $302.10
8. $226.00; $198.10
9. $369.00; $240.35
10. $194.40; $161.65
11. $366.00; $293.19
12. $238.40; $187.60
13. $278.00; $194.80
14. $177.72
15. $894.20
16. $213.05
17. $299.49

Page 28

1. food
2. $920.50
3. Rent/mortgage payment
4. $2,380.00
5. No. They overspent by $15.00.

Page 30

Monthly variable expenses	
	$1,105.00
Monthly fixed expenses	1,823.00
Annual expenses	3,525.00
Monthly share	293.75
Total monthly expenses	3,221.75
Balance	178.25

Page 31

1. $1,105.00
2. $1,823.00
3. $3,525.00
4. $293.75
5. $3,400.00
6. $3,221.75
7. Yes
8. Underspent by $178.25
9. $60.00
10. $55.00
11. $95.00
12. $85.50
13. $75.60
14. $287.00
15. $220.00
16. $42.04
17. $73.40
18. $98.00
19. $47.00
20. $204.00

Page 32

1. $76.67
2. $98.33
3. $78.67
4. $57.67
5. $46.00
6. $146.67
7. $600.00

Page 33

8. $850.00
9. $458.75
10. $170.00
11. $156.25
12. $77.50
13. $150.00
14. $177.50
15. $24.75
16. $49.50
17. $52.00
18. $333.75
19. $2,500.00
20. $2,500.00
21. $458.75
22. mortgage, insurance
23. $333.75
24. $77.50
25. $156.25

Page 35

Food	$515	Rent/Mort.	$675
Elec.	0	Car Pay.	250
Heat/AC	60	Appl.	0
Tel.	22	Furn.	30
Water	0	Sav.	200
TV	48	Emerg.	70
Gas/Oil	75	TOTAL	1,225
Parking	20		
Tolls	0	Life Ins.	300
Repairs	50	Home Ins.	0
Other	0	Car Ins.	475
Clothing	85	Med. Ins.	2,800
Credit	75	RE Tax	0
Gifts	45	Medical	1,200
Contrib.	50	TOTAL	4,775
Movies/Sports	80	MO. SHARE	397.92
Mag/Papers	25	Budget	3,100
Dining	70	Var. Exp.	1,220
TOTAL	1,220	F. Exp.	1,225
		A. Exp.	397.92
		MO. EXP	2,842.92
		BALANCE	257.08

No. The budget does not have to be revised; the balance can be added to savings.

Page 36
1. 297.5
2. 223.8
3. 88.16
4. 63.7
5. 2.982
6. 69.92
7. 85.54
8. .15642

Page 37
9. .018
10. .01644
11. .30668
12. .010608
13. 724.5
14. 1,741.32
15. 23.244
16. 1.752
17. .0034
18. .006981
19. $30.66
20. $24.75
21. $9.60
22. $15.84
23. $162.97
24. $17.20
25. $7.54
26. $8.01
27. $42.53
28. $143.25
29. $58.60
30. $89.91

Page 39
1. $152.35
2. $114.91
3. $507.73
4. $770.06
5. $1,779.28
6. $847.72
7. $3,328.14
8. $96.50
9. $579.21
10. $1,263.95
11. $394.92
12. $451.45
13. $373.48
14. $618.22
15. $50.00
16. $130.95
17. $513.48

Page 41
1. $410.00; $15.00
2. $963.00; $88.00
3. $573.70; $48.70
4. $627.20; $27.20
5. $2,951.60; $101.60
6. $306.90; $16.90
7. $395.50; $20.50
8. $15,194.00; $244.00
9. $930.20; $30.20
10. $435.00; $40.00
11. $4,550.00; $300.0
12. $999.40; $84.40
13. $125.00; $500.00
14. $129.50; $1,165.50
15. $270.00; $1,530.00
16. $298.50; $696.50
17. $19.80; $145.20
18. $90.00; $360.00
19. $89.50; $805.50
20. $180.00; $540.00
21. $2,511.00; $11,439.00
22. $210.00; $315.00

Page 43
1. $2,373.00; $373.00
2. $1,948.80; $148.80
3. $1,092.50; $142.50
4. $12,999.84; $2,999.84
5. $29,527.20; $1,027.20
6. $429.90; $29.90
7. $2,551.80; $351.80
8. $18,119.88; $1,619.88
9. $5,604.30; $604.30
10. $1,683.00; $183.00
11. $4,868.64; $368.64
12. $23,556.00; $1,056.00
13. $3,137.28; $637.28
14. $5,335.20; $1,135.20
15. $161.25

Page 45
1. $45.12
2. $63.80
3. $91.68
4. $34.31

5. $17.58; $210.96; $10.96
6. $62.38; $1,122.84; $122.84
7. $131.87; $1,582.44; $82.44
8. $49.92; $1,198.08; $198.08
9. $23.07; $553.68; $53.68
10. $93.57; $1,684.26; $184.26
11. $49.48; $1,187.52; $187.52
12. $35.10; $210.60; $10.60
13. $69.21; $1,661.04; $161.04
14. $45.84; $550.08; $50.08
15. $90.25; $1,083.00; $83.00
16. $142.92

Page 46
1. 16
2. 21.6
3. 480
4. 11.4
5. 3
6. 36
7. 6.8
8. 31.44
9. 4.5
10. 30
11. 18
12. 240
13. 18
14. 12.4
15. 14
16. 80
17. 14
18. 60

Page 47
1. 6.48
2. .053
3. 119.14
4. .64
5. .0896
6. 19.7
7. 3.6
8. 47.34
9. .0086
10. .393
11. 1.86
12. .0094

Page 48
1. i
2. f
3. e
4. a
5. c
6. h
7. j
8. b
9. k
10. d
11. $120.00
12. $144.00
13. $170.00
14. $255.00
15. $50.00

Page 49
16. 24.358
17. 4.582
18. 152.1

19. 28.9
20. 43
21. 7,028
22. 289
23. 93
24. 15.27
25. .07
26. 7.6
27. .43
28. .88
29. 57%
30. 6.2%
31. $17.20; $68.80
32. $37.50; $212.50
33. $210.00; $630.00
34. $72.00; $528.00
35. $330.00; $1,870.00

Page 51
1. $24,100.00
2. $25,740.00
3. $36,517.00
4. $21,370.25
5. $750.00; $19,565.00
6. $1,167.50; $24,565.50
7. $1,095.00; $19,380.00
8. $955.80; $24,902.80
9. $1,088.75; $22,902.50
10. $1,190.40; $21,072.90
11. $871.75; $18,333.75
12. $892.60; $23,240.10
13. $1,722.00; $26,367.00
14. $1,641.00; $29,043.75
15. $765.00; $16,108.50

Page 53
1. $1,570.00
2. $1,878.50
3. $1,089.00
4. $924.75
5. $3,052.50
6. $523.20
7. $1,275.00; $7,494.00;
   $8,769.00
8. $3,590.00; $18,435.60;
   $22,025.60
9. $1,280.00; $11,900.00;
   $13,180.00
10. $6,537.50; $26,400.00;
    $32,937.50
11. $2,962.50; $7,512.00;
    $10,474.50
12. $1,080.00; $12,800.00;
    $13,880.00
13. $2,846.50; $28,932.00;
    $31,778.50
14. $2,232.00; $16,764.00;
    $18,996.00

15. $3,030.00; $15,375.60;
    $18,405.60
16. $1,417.50; $6,802.20;
    $8,219.70
17. $3,855.00; $12,237.50;
    $16,092.50
18. $1,573.00; $14,028.00;
    $15,601.00
19. $25,840.84
20. $170.00

Page 54
1. $2,800; $.28
2. $2,320; $.29
3. $3,240; $.27
4. $4,800; $.24
5. $3,750; $.25
6. $2,850; $.30
7. $5,572; $.31
8. $3,274; $.33
9. $3,894; $.19
10. $2,180; $.27
11. $4,380; $.23
12. $2,195; $.44
13. $3,935; $.26
14. $3,010; $.12

Page 55
15. $.03
16. $.06
17. $.04
18. $.05
19. $.25
20. $.275 or 27.5¢

Page 57
1. $105.50
2. $110.75
3. $387.85
4. $95.65; $311.10
5. $110.75; $310.00
6. $102.00; $308.10
7. $145.95; $391.35
8. $115.10; $340.60
9. $104.50; $348.80
10. $131.65; $336.25
11. $90.50; $320.30
12. $125.90; $359.95
13. $112.85; $352.45
14. $120.40; $341.25
15. $99.50; $292.47

Page 59
1. 9.4   16. .16
2. 29.8   17. 94
3. 2.39   18. 1.59
4. .63   19. 2.6
5. 18.6   20. 95
6. 9.8   21. .52
7. 51   22. 8.62
8. 4,270   23. 25
9. 810   24. .6
10. 20   25. 5.2
11. 8.4   26. 2,400
12. 4.1   27. 65
13. 39   28. 730
14. 1.4   29. $1.28
15. 40   30. $1.52

Page 61
1. $33,000.00; $132,000.00
2. $18,500.00; $166,500.00
3. $25,320.00; $143,480.00
4. $23,125.00; $69,375.00
5. $16,500.00; $93,500.00
6. $151,740.00
7. $236,700.00
8. $163,710.00
9. $269,424.00
10. $329,832.00
11. $256,446.00; $104,446.00
12. $172,872.00; $32,872.00
13. $213,240.00; $75,740.00
14. $187,308.00; $27,308.00
15. $240,075.00; $90,075.00

Page 63
1. $1,215.00
2. $1,475.60
3. $1,432.56
4. $1,422.36
5. $1,911.05
6. $1,429.50
7. $1,090.80
8. $1,176.00; $352,800.00
9. $2,315.25; $833,490.00
10. $1,661.52; $398,764.80
11. $1,494.00; $358,560.00
12. $1,669.44; $500,832.00
13. $2,001.84; $720,662.40
14. $1,633.70; $490,110.00
15. $1,177.20; $353,160.00
16. $1,449.00; $521,640.00
17. $2,066.00; $495,840.00

Page 65
1. 20
2. 400
3. 850
4. 1,250
5. 625
6. 1,025
7. $75,000.00
8. $96,000.00
9. $70,000.00
10. $99,000.00
11. $60,500.00
12. $56,800.00
13. $111,600.00
14. $100,500.00
15. $79,750.00
16. $113,750.00
17. $5,100.00
18. $4,410.00
19. $3,705.00
20. $4,600.00
21. $85,200.00; $3,408.00
22. $112,500.00; $4,950.00
23. $70,000.00; $2,975.00
24. $82,750.00; $5,130.50
25. $50,400.00; $1,965.60

Page 67
1. $459.00
2. $600.00
3. $482.00
4. $890.00
5. $537.00
6. $508.00
7. $789.00
8. $510.00
9. $75,000.00; $15,000.00;
   $30,000.00
10. $70,000.00; $14,000.00;
    $28,000.00
11. $85,000.00; $17,000.00;
    $34,000.00
12. $90,000.00; $18,000.00;
    $36,000.00
13. $110,000.00; $22,000.00;
    $44,000.00
14. $125,000.00; $25,000.00;
    $50,000.00
15. $150,000.00; $30,000.00;
    $60,000.00

Page 68
1. 50%
2. 75%
3. 50%
4. 20%
5. $33\frac{1}{3}$%
6. 60%
7. $66\frac{2}{3}$%
8. 25%
9. 85%
10. 25%

11. $31\frac{1}{4}$%
12. 24%
13. $7\frac{1}{2}$%
14. 50%
15. 30%
16. $37\frac{1}{2}$%
17. 38%
18. $53\frac{1}{3}$%
19. 30%
20. 32%

Page 69
1. $\frac{1}{2}$
2. $\frac{3}{4}$
3. $\frac{2}{5}$
4. $\frac{1}{4}$
5. $\frac{3}{4}$
6. $\frac{1}{3}$
7. $\frac{2}{3}$
8. $\frac{14}{25}$
9. $\frac{5}{6}$
10. $\frac{3}{4}$
11. $\frac{1}{2}$
12. $\frac{6}{7}$
13. $\frac{1}{3}$
14. $\frac{3}{5}$
15. $\frac{1}{2}$
16. $\frac{2}{3}$

17. $\frac{1}{3}$
18. $\frac{7}{8}$
19. $\frac{3}{8}$
20. $\frac{17}{25}$
21. $\frac{2}{5}$
22. $\frac{2}{3}$
23. $\frac{4}{5}$
24. $\frac{3}{4}$
25. $\frac{4}{5}$
26. $\frac{1}{5}$
27. $\frac{1}{5}$
28. $\frac{7}{10}$
29. $\frac{5}{8}$
30. $\frac{12}{25}$

Page 71
1. $.05
2. $.10
3. $.26
4. $.51
5. $1.17
6. $.79
7. $1.25; $22.04
8. $.59; $10.34
9. $.60; $10.55
10. $.79; $13.94
11. $13.98; $363.48
12. $59.70; $1,054.70
13. $2.00; $51.95
14. $.88; $18.38
15. $1.44; $25.39
16. $19.00; $494.00
17. $.83; $17.33
18. $48.65; $743.65
19. $2.88; $50.83
20. $.33; $6.98

Page 72
1. $1,239.15
2. $1,502.00
3. $3,045.90
4. $2,937.60
5. $1,162.50

6. $3,110.25
7. $1,581.00
8. $2,922.30
9. $3,499.66
10. $2,752.42

Page 73
11. $1,751.75
12. $3,687.30
13. $2,478.30
14. $3,004.00
15. $6,091.80
16. $5,875.20
17. $2,325.00
18. $6,220.50
19. $3,162.00
20. $5,844.60
21. $6,999.32
22. $5,504.83
23. $5,362.14
24. $7,374.60
25. $6,759.00

Page 75
1. $32,965.50
2. $26,936.50
3. $25,765.00
4. $28,405.90
5. $15,150.00
6. $7,500.00

Page 76
1. $45,570.00
2. $17,350.00
3. $34,050.00
4. $40,355.00

Page 77
5. $5,000.00; $30,325.00
6. $7,500.00; $43,175.00
7. $2,500.00; $23,172.00
8. $7,500.00; $25,775.00
9. $5,000.00; $39,255.00
10. $2,500.00; $19,325.00
11. $7,500.00; $40,825.00
12. $10,000.00; $40,080.00
13. $5,000.00; $61,488.00
14. $12,500.00; $21,905.00
15. 0; $21,389.00
16. $2,500.00; $15,097.00
17. $34,190.00
18. $57,920.00
19. $26,244.00
20. $32,550.00

Page 79
1. $920.00
2. $757.50

3. $1,424.00
4. $1,370.00
5. $1,637.00
6. $1,715.00
7. $1,920.00
8. $5,840.00
9. $1,245.90
10. $2,060.00
11. $613.00
12. $603.00
13. $653.00
14. $683.00
15. $728.00
16. $573.00
17. $548.00
18. $698.00

Page 80
1. $\frac{5}{6}$
2. $\frac{3}{4}$
3. 1
4. $\frac{5}{8}$
5. $1\frac{1}{2}$
6. $1\frac{1}{4}$
7. $1\frac{3}{8}$
8. $\frac{1}{2}$
9. $1\frac{1}{6}$
10. $\frac{3}{4}$
11. $1\frac{5}{12}$
12. $1\frac{3}{8}$

Page 81
13. $1\frac{1}{12}$
14. $\frac{1}{2}$
15. $\frac{19}{24}$
16. $1\frac{1}{24}$
17. $1\frac{1}{6}$
18. $1\frac{7}{10}$
19. $\frac{1}{4}$
20. $\frac{3}{8}$
21. $\frac{1}{2}$
22. $\frac{1}{8}$
23. $\frac{3}{16}$
24. $\frac{1}{6}$
25. $\frac{1}{3}$
26. $\frac{1}{6}$
27. $\frac{5}{12}$
28. $\frac{3}{10}$
29. $\frac{5}{24}$
30. $\frac{1}{6}$
31. $\frac{1}{16}$
32. $\frac{7}{32}$
33. $\frac{2}{15}$
34. $\frac{2}{3}$
35. $\frac{1}{16}$
36. $\frac{1}{12}$
37. $1\frac{1}{4}$ hours
38. $1\frac{1}{8}$ hours

Page 83
1. $2,155.75
2. $5,919.03
3. $6,646.19
4. $20,398.40
5. 1.061831; $1,061.83;
    $61.83
6. 1.198693; $599.35;
    $99.35
7. 1.715921; $4,289.80;
    $1,789.80
8. 1.349817; $5,399.27;
    $1,399.27
9. 1.017408; $5,595.74;
    $95.74

10. 1.591936; $11,143.55;
    $4,143.55
11. 1.271224; $4,449.28;
    $949.28
12. 1.615989; $9,695.93;
    $3,695.93
13. 1.309932; $11,134.42;
    $2,634.42
14. 1.785936; $3,571.87;
    $1,571.87
15. 1.019920; $12,239.04;
    $239.04
16. $6,816.90; $1,816.90

Page 85
1. $3,750.00
2. $4,950.00
3. $21,250.00
4. $15,512.50
5. $8.00; $4,800.00;
    $4,884.75
6. $39.625; $15,850.00;
    $15,920.90
7. $31.25; $4,687.50;
    $4,729.15
8. $21.75; $1,087.50;
    $1,107.65
9. $30.50; $3,050.00;
    $3,082.95
10. $44.75; $53,700.00;
    $53,847.25
11. $30.125; $7,531.25;
    $7,593.00
12. $20.25; $40,500.00;
    $40,710.00
13. $12.875; $2,575.00;
    $2,623.20
14. $43.25; $43,250.00;
    $43,380.60
15. $7.375; $5,531.25;
    $5,624.05
16. $14.75; $14,750.00;
    $14,875.15
17. $8,353.90
18. $12,885.50

Page 86
19. $2,663.50; $238.08
20. $2,602.25; $161.00
21. $3,107.50; $220.98
22. $5,964.10; $152.35
23. $16,914.75; $643.85
24. $750.90
25. $329.25

Page 87
1. 25%
2. 40%
3. 50%
4. $12\frac{1}{2}$%
5. 35%
6. 75%
7. 90%
8. $37\frac{1}{2}$%
9. 32%
10. 18%
11. $17\frac{1}{2}$%
12. $33\frac{1}{3}$%
13. 95%
14. 70%
15. $7\frac{1}{2}$%
16. 36%
17. $62\frac{1}{2}$%
18. $83\frac{1}{3}$%
19. 80%
20. $87\frac{1}{2}$%
21. 60%
22. 55%
23. $66\frac{2}{3}$%
24. 64%
25. 70%

Page 88
1. $1,245.00
2. $835.00
3. $2,700.00
4. $7,525.00

Page 89
5. $200.00
6. $130.00
7. $350.00
8. $217.50
9. $2,400.00; $200.00
10. $1,300.00; $110.00
11. $1,800.00; $157.50
12. $670.00; $62.50
13. $8,200.00; $750.00
14. $3,900.00; $390.00
15. $36,000.00; $3,500.00
16. $1,600.00; $162.50
17. $9,500.00; $875.00
18. $1,650.00; $150.00
19. $3,275.00; $250.00
20. $3,768.75; $450.00

Page 91
1. $50
2. $125
3. $25
4. $500
5. $5,000
6. $2,750
7. $329.20
8. $853.60
9. $36.12
10. $4,646
11. $100; $36.12;
    $144.48; $44.48
12. $50; $28.14;
    $56.28; $6.28
13. $250; $42.68;
    $426.80; $176.80
14. $500; $50.64;
    $1,012.80; $512.80

15. $25; $39.24;
$39.24; $14.24
16. $5,000; $46.46;
$9,292.00; $4,292.00
17. $2,500; $27.22;
$2,722.00; $222.00
18. $200; $28.14;
$225.12; $25.12
19. $400; $30.28;
$484.48; $84.48
20. $325; $32.92;
$427.96; $102.96

Page 92
1. $650.00
2. $6,950

Page 93
3. 8%
4. 12%
5. $116.00; 8%
6. $580.00; 8%
7. $193.50; 6%
8. $213.00; 5%
9. $180.00; $7\frac{1}{2}$%
10. $1,530.00; 12%
11. $994.50; 5%
12. $12,500.00; 10%
13. $4,104.00; 8%
14. $702.00; 6%
15. $1,337.50; 7.4%

Page 94
16. $2,400; $120; 5%
17. $2,400; $240; 10%
18. $3,600; $450; $12\frac{1}{2}$%
19. $20,000; $1,600; 8%
20. $1,875; $150; 8%
21. $7,000; $700; 10%
22. $5,200; $650; $12\frac{1}{2}$%
23. $6,000; $720; 12%
24. $6,080; $760; $12\frac{1}{2}$%
25. $12\frac{1}{2}$%

Page 95
1. False
2. True
3. False
4. False
5. True
6. True
7. True
8. True
9. False
10. False
11. $3.75; $66.25
12. $.16; $2.25
13. $26.60; $406.60
14. $1.04; $13.99
15. $1.63; $26.63

Page 96
16. $1\frac{5}{12}$
17. $\frac{1}{2}$
18. $\frac{3}{4}$
19. $\frac{1}{6}$
20. $\frac{1}{4}$
21. $\frac{1}{8}$
22. $23,002.20
23. $22,527.20
24. $10,159.75
25. $1,507.85
26. 35%
27. 80%
28. 55%
29. 95%
30. 60%

Using Fractions

Page 5
A.

1. 19	**2.** 10	**3.** 7
4. 31	**5.** 259	**6.** 4
7. 3	**8.** 2	**9.** 514
10. 22	**11.** 0	**12.** 3
13. 235	**14.** 581	**15.** 316
16. 5	**17.** 7	**18.** 8
19. 9	**20.** 5	**21.** 4,284
22. 152	**23.** $21.90	**24.** 1R7
25. 129	**26.** $44.85	**27.** 1,404
28. 34R3	**29.** 1,614	**30.** $23.22

Page 6
B.

1. 20	**2.** 8	**3.** 291
4. 5,877	**5.** 3R4	**6.** $165.63
7. 38,292	**8.** 21R8	**9.** $8.23
10. 8	**11.** 8,439	**12.** 64R1
13. 42R12	**14.** $1.15	**15.** 3,690
16. 24R12	**17.** 44,820	**18.** $24.99
19. $1.35	**20.** $1.72	**21.** 1,244
22. $784.07	**23.** 4,572	**24.** 37R1
25. $28.12	**26.** 11R8	**27.** 1,573
28. $359.24	**29.** 7,028	**30.** 14

Page 7
C.

1. 127	**2.** 79	**3.** 5,722
4. 22,102	**5.** 55R8	**6.** $\frac{3}{5}$
7. 214,790	**8.** $\frac{3}{8}$	**9.** $\frac{21}{40}$
10. $\frac{15}{16}$	**11.** $\frac{2}{3}$	**12.** 192
13. $\frac{1}{2}$	**14.** $\frac{1}{9}$	**15.** $\frac{3}{20}$
16. 9	**17.** $.27	**18.** 24
19. 294,378	**20.** 25	**21.** 16,132
22. $192.92	**23.** $129.30	**24.** 11,488
25. 49R21	**26.** 135R2	**27.** $790.46
28. $759.88	**29.** $\frac{1}{5}$	**30.** $\frac{1}{4}$

Page 8
D.

1. $.56
2. $48.00
3. $692.48
4. $\frac{1}{2}$ pound
5. $146.25
6. $20,280.00
7. yes; no
8. $7,800
9. $32.67

Page 9

1. 6   **2.** 5   **3.** $\frac{5}{6}$

Page 10

1. $\frac{1}{8}$	**6.** $\frac{3}{4}$
2. $\frac{2}{3}$	**7.** $\frac{7}{8}$
3. $\frac{3}{10}$	**8.** $\frac{1}{4}$
4. $\frac{5}{12}$	**9.** $\frac{4}{7}$
5. $\frac{1}{2}$	**10.** $\frac{5}{12}$

Page 11

1. improper	**9.** proper
2. mixed	**10.** mixed
3. proper	**11.** proper
4. mixed	**12.** mixed
5. improper	**13.** mixed
6. improper	**14.** mixed
7. improper	**15.** mixed
8. improper	**16.** proper

Page 12
A.

2. $\frac{4}{5}$	**10.** $\frac{1}{3}$
3. $\frac{1}{4}$	**11.** $\frac{1}{3}$
4. $\frac{1}{2}$	**12.** $\frac{4}{9}$
5. $\frac{1}{4}$	**13.** $\frac{1}{4}$
6. $\frac{1}{4}$	**14.** $\frac{1}{6}$
7. $\frac{2}{5}$	**15.** $\frac{1}{7}$
8. $\frac{3}{8}$	**16.** $\frac{1}{8}$
9. $\frac{1}{2}$	

Page 13
B.

2. $\frac{3}{5}$	**21.** $\frac{3}{8}$
3. $\frac{1}{2}$	**22.** $\frac{11}{20}$
4. $\frac{1}{2}$	**23.** $\frac{2}{3}$
5. $\frac{5}{6}$	**24.** $\frac{7}{9}$
6. $\frac{2}{3}$	**25.** $\frac{2}{3}$
7. $\frac{7}{9}$	**26.** $\frac{7}{12}$
8. $\frac{1}{4}$	**27.** $\frac{2}{9}$
9. $\frac{1}{5}$	**28.** $\frac{4}{5}$
10. $\frac{1}{6}$	**29.** $\frac{1}{2}$
11. $\frac{5}{9}$	**30.** $\frac{3}{7}$
12. $\frac{1}{7}$	**31.** $\frac{1}{7}$
13. $\frac{2}{11}$	**32.** $\frac{1}{7}$
14. $\frac{7}{8}$	**33.** $\frac{4}{21}$
15. $\frac{1}{3}$	**34.** $\frac{3}{8}$
16. $\frac{15}{16}$	**35.** $\frac{3}{11}$
17. $\frac{2}{3}$	**36.** $\frac{2}{3}$
18. $\frac{2}{3}$	**37.** $\frac{5}{7}$
19. $\frac{3}{5}$	**38.** $\frac{1}{3}$
20. $\frac{1}{3}$	**39.** $\frac{1}{3}$
	40. $\frac{3}{4}$

Page 14
A.

1. 7	**2.** $6\frac{3}{4}$	**3.** $2\frac{2}{3}$
4. $3\frac{1}{2}$	**5.** $4\frac{1}{2}$	**6.** 12
7. $2\frac{2}{5}$	**8.** 3	**9.** 1
10. $11\frac{1}{3}$	**11.** $3\frac{2}{3}$	**12.** $6\frac{2}{3}$
13. $5\frac{2}{11}$	**14.** $7\frac{3}{7}$	**15.** $3\frac{4}{5}$
16. $1\frac{3}{7}$	**17.** $3\frac{1}{4}$	**18.** $2\frac{5}{6}$

B.

1. $2\frac{1}{5}$	**2.** $8\frac{3}{4}$	**3.** $2\frac{1}{2}$
4. 6	**5.** $3\frac{1}{5}$	**6.** $1\frac{1}{2}$
7. $2\frac{1}{3}$	**8.** $4\frac{1}{5}$	**9.** $2\frac{2}{7}$
10. 6	**11.** 3	**12.** 1
13. $3\frac{1}{3}$	**14.** $6\frac{4}{7}$	**15.** 2
14. $2\frac{11}{14}$	**15.** $4\frac{1}{3}$	**18.** $8\frac{1}{2}$

Page 15

C.

1. $\frac{11}{4}$
2. $\frac{69}{11}$
3. $\frac{13}{3}$
4. $\frac{36}{7}$
5. $\frac{101}{8}$
6. $\frac{74}{9}$
7. $\frac{9}{4}$
8. $\frac{23}{5}$
9. $\frac{23}{9}$
10. $\frac{17}{5}$

D.

1. $\frac{103}{11}$
2. $\frac{7}{3}$
3. $\frac{76}{9}$
4. $\frac{13}{2}$
5. $\frac{47}{8}$
6. $\frac{5}{4}$
7. $\frac{17}{3}$
8. $\frac{57}{8}$
9. $\frac{101}{12}$
10. $\frac{9}{2}$

Page 16
A.

1. fraction
2. proper
3. numerator
4. improper
5. denominator
6. mixed

B.

1. improper
2. mixed
3. improper
4. proper
5. mixed
6. improper
7. proper
8. mixed
9. proper
10. improper
11. mixed
12. mixed
13. improper
14. proper
15. proper

16. mixed
17. proper
18. improper

Page 17
C.

1. $\frac{23}{8}$
2. $\frac{7}{4}$
3. $\frac{44}{7}$
4. $\frac{11}{6}$
5. $\frac{29}{3}$
6. $\frac{17}{2}$
7. $\frac{61}{12}$
8. $\frac{43}{10}$
9. $\frac{9}{4}$
10. $\frac{27}{8}$
11. $\frac{20}{19}$
12. $\frac{47}{16}$

D.

1. 5
2. $1\frac{1}{7}$
3. $10\frac{5}{7}$
4. $2\frac{1}{2}$
5. $15\frac{5}{8}$
6. 7
7. $7\frac{7}{8}$
8. 4
9. $18\frac{1}{2}$
10. $3\frac{19}{27}$
11. 9
12. 7

Pages 18–19
A.

1. $\frac{3}{5}$ 2. $1\frac{1}{2}$ 3. $\frac{1}{2}$ 4. $\frac{1}{2}$
5. $\frac{5}{7}$ 6. $\frac{2}{3}$ 7. 1 8. 1
9. $1\frac{1}{4}$ 10. $\frac{7}{8}$ 11. $\frac{5}{7}$ 12. $\frac{1}{4}$
13. $\frac{2}{3}$ 14. 1 15. $1\frac{1}{2}$ 16. $1\frac{1}{3}$

Page 20
B.

1. 9 2. $7\frac{2}{7}$ 3. $7\frac{2}{3}$
4. 8 5. 5 6. $6\frac{1}{2}$
7. 9 8. 8 9. $25\frac{2}{3}$
10. $8\frac{4}{5}$ 11. $8\frac{1}{5}$ 12. 11
13. $9\frac{5}{8}$ 14. $16\frac{3}{4}$ 15. $12\frac{1}{7}$
16. 14 17. 6 18. $18\frac{1}{3}$

Page 21
C.

1. 14 2. $28\frac{1}{4}$ 3. 33
4. $18\frac{5}{8}$ 5. $25\frac{15}{16}$ 6. $13\frac{1}{2}$
7. $47\frac{3}{8}$ 8. 30 9. 45
10. $30\frac{11}{25}$ 11. $16\frac{9}{16}$ 12. $15\frac{4}{5}$
13. $16\frac{1}{5}$ 14. $19\frac{13}{16}$ 15. $20\frac{14}{15}$
16. $36\frac{3}{4}$ 17. $5\frac{1}{4}$ 18. $48\frac{3}{5}$

Pages 23–24
A.

1. $1\frac{5}{8}$ 2. $1\frac{1}{6}$ 3. $\frac{4}{5}$
4. $8\frac{8}{9}$ 5. $7\frac{3}{4}$ 6. $6\frac{13}{16}$
7. $9\frac{19}{20}$ 8. $7\frac{1}{12}$ 9. $\frac{35}{36}$
10. $8\frac{19}{24}$ 11. $2\frac{15}{56}$ 12. $7\frac{9}{20}$
13. $5\frac{5}{6}$ 14. $9\frac{1}{24}$ 15. $11\frac{1}{30}$

B.

1. $6\frac{5}{6}$ 2. $10\frac{17}{20}$ 3. $6\frac{1}{2}$
4. $15\frac{3}{8}$ 5. $11\frac{20}{21}$ 6. $8\frac{5}{12}$
7. $25\frac{3}{16}$ 8. $22\frac{11}{40}$ 9. $4\frac{7}{12}$

Page 25

1. $\frac{5}{6}$ 2. $3\frac{7}{12}$ 3. $1\frac{1}{12}$ 4. $1\frac{2}{3}$
5. $6\frac{4}{5}$ 6. $9\frac{23}{24}$ 7. $6\frac{11}{18}$ 8. $7\frac{11}{28}$
9. $14\frac{17}{42}$ 10. $11\frac{1}{8}$ 11. $15\frac{3}{4}$ 12. $13\frac{19}{20}$
13. $18\frac{2}{3}$ 14. $5\frac{29}{35}$ 15. $16\frac{5}{12}$ 16. $41\frac{7}{24}$

Page 26
A.

1. $1\frac{1}{2}$
2. 1
3. $1\frac{1}{8}$
4. 2
5. $1\frac{1}{3}$
6. $1\frac{2}{5}$
7. 5
8. 4
9. $4\frac{1}{8}$
10. $1\frac{1}{2}$

B.

1. $\frac{2}{5}$
2. $\frac{1}{2}$
3. $\frac{3}{4}$
4. $\frac{1}{4}$
5. $\frac{1}{3}$
6. $\frac{2}{3}$
7. $\frac{2}{5}$
8. $\frac{1}{4}$
9. $\frac{3}{8}$
10. $\frac{1}{2}$

C.

1. $\frac{3}{2}$ 2. $\frac{8}{5}$ 3. $\frac{41}{8}$
4. $\frac{21}{4}$ 5. $\frac{10}{3}$ 6. $\frac{17}{6}$
7. $\frac{23}{7}$ 8. $\frac{82}{9}$ 9. $\frac{7}{6}$

Page 27
D.

1. $\frac{3}{5}$ 2. $\frac{2}{3}$ 3. $\frac{1}{2}$ 4. $15\frac{5}{24}$
5. $\frac{5}{7}$ 6. $7\frac{1}{16}$ 7. $23\frac{9}{14}$ 8. $15\frac{17}{18}$
9. $11\frac{5}{6}$ 10. $22\frac{7}{9}$ 11. $18\frac{11}{24}$ 12. $47\frac{7}{16}$
13. $11\frac{1}{4}$ 14. $20\frac{1}{3}$ 15. $10\frac{37}{42}$ 16. $21\frac{1}{8}$
17. $30\frac{37}{44}$ 18. $16\frac{39}{112}$ 19. $14\frac{23}{28}$ 20. $8\frac{5}{12}$
21. $14\frac{7}{8}$ 22. $5\frac{19}{24}$ 23. $17\frac{11}{30}$ 24. $8\frac{1}{18}$
25. $35\frac{13}{30}$ 26. $5\frac{1}{24}$ 27. $9\frac{7}{8}$ 28. $15\frac{5}{7}$

Page 28
A.

1. 7 1 $\frac{1}{2}$ $4\frac{1}{4}$
2. $2\frac{1}{2}$ $6\frac{1}{4}$ $7\frac{1}{4}$ $2\frac{2}{7}$
3. $3\frac{1}{3}$ 2 $3\frac{1}{4}$ $3\frac{1}{6}$

Pages 30–31
B.

1. $3\frac{2}{3}$ 5. $3\frac{1}{3}$
2. $5\frac{2}{5}$ 6. $1\frac{1}{2}$
3. $1\frac{1}{3}$ 7. $4\frac{1}{2}$
4. $5\frac{1}{4}$

Pages 32–33
C.

1. $2\frac{1}{6}$ 7. $2\frac{7}{8}$
2. $3\frac{1}{2}$ 8. $8\frac{3}{4}$
3. $3\frac{3}{5}$ 9. $6\frac{4}{5}$
4. $2\frac{7}{8}$ 10. $6\frac{6}{7}$
5. $8\frac{1}{3}$ 11. $6\frac{3}{4}$
6. $7\frac{15}{16}$ 12. $\frac{1}{8}$

Pages 35–36
A.

1. $2\frac{11}{12}$ 6. $2\frac{7}{8}$
2. $7\frac{5}{8}$ 7. $1\frac{8}{9}$
3. $4\frac{3}{8}$ 8. $4\frac{7}{8}$
4. $3\frac{9}{16}$ 9. $2\frac{5}{12}$
5. 2 10. $\frac{5}{6}$

Page 37
B.

1. $3\frac{1}{3}$
2. $6\frac{11}{20}$
3. $3\frac{1}{8}$
4. $4\frac{11}{20}$
5. $8\frac{5}{12}$
6. $1\frac{19}{21}$
7. $5\frac{7}{8}$
8. $1\frac{29}{30}$

Page 38
C.

1. $5\frac{1}{6}$
2. $\frac{5}{8}$
3. $2\frac{13}{18}$
4. $1\frac{5}{8}$
5. $1\frac{1}{2}$
6 $4\frac{3}{14}$
7. $\frac{3}{4}$
8. $17\frac{5}{6}$

Page 39
A.

1. $\frac{1}{4}$
2. $\frac{2}{7}$
3. $\frac{1}{3}$
4. $\frac{1}{2}$
5. $\frac{15}{16}$
6. $\frac{1}{5}$
7. $\frac{3}{11}$
8. $\frac{3}{4}$
9. $\frac{2}{3}$
10. $\frac{4}{5}$
11. $\frac{1}{4}$
12. $\frac{1}{4}$

B.

1. 1
2. $2\frac{1}{5}$
3. $1\frac{5}{8}$
4. $5\frac{2}{3}$
5. 2
6. $3\frac{1}{13}$
7. $2\frac{1}{4}$
8. 4
9. $1\frac{1}{5}$
10. $1\frac{1}{8}$
11. $2\frac{3}{4}$
12. 3

Page 40

C.
1. $\frac{4}{3}$
2. $\frac{11}{5}$
3. $\frac{5}{2}$
4. $\frac{25}{8}$
5. $\frac{5}{4}$
6. $\frac{20}{9}$
7. $\frac{9}{7}$
8. $\frac{13}{6}$
9. $\frac{15}{8}$
10. $\frac{32}{3}$

D.
1. $\frac{2}{3}$
2. $\frac{3}{4}$
3. $7\frac{1}{8}$
4. $1\frac{1}{5}$
5. $13\frac{5}{12}$
6. $9\frac{3}{16}$
7. $5\frac{3}{8}$
8. $4\frac{5}{6}$
9. $8\frac{17}{42}$
10. $1\frac{3}{8}$

Page 41

E.
1. 6
2. $9\frac{1}{5}$
3. $\frac{3}{4}$
4. $3\frac{1}{3}$
5. $5\frac{3}{8}$
6. $4\frac{9}{14}$
7. $\frac{24}{35}$
8. $1\frac{7}{12}$
9. $1\frac{13}{24}$
10. $1\frac{5}{6}$

Page 42

A.
1. $\frac{1}{12}$
2. $\frac{3}{8}$
3. $\frac{5}{12}$

B.
1. $\frac{5}{16}$
2. $\frac{7}{16}$
3. $\frac{27}{80}$
4. $\frac{5}{24}$
5. $\frac{8}{81}$
6. $\frac{6}{45}$
7. $\frac{15}{30}$
8. $\frac{3}{16}$
9. $\frac{5}{27}$
10. $\frac{1}{36}$

11. $\frac{1}{50}$
12. $\frac{3}{12}$
13. $\frac{1}{4}$
14. $\frac{30}{42}$
15. $\frac{6}{72}$
16. $\frac{16}{77}$

Page 43

C.
1. $\frac{1}{14}$
2. $\frac{1}{15}$
3. $\frac{1}{6}$
4. $\frac{1}{32}$
5. $\frac{1}{90}$
6. $\frac{6}{81}$
7. $\frac{1}{56}$
8. $\frac{3}{22}$
9. $\frac{6}{15}$
10. $\frac{25}{42}$
11. $\frac{6}{72}$
12. $\frac{10}{56}$
13. $\frac{10}{27}$
14. $\frac{1}{20}$
15. $\frac{21}{40}$
16. $\frac{18}{48}$
17. $\frac{4}{10}$
18. $\frac{20}{54}$
19. $\frac{4}{21}$
20. $\frac{3}{30}$
21. $\frac{2}{6}$
22. $\frac{42}{56}$
23. $\frac{15}{45}$
24. $\frac{7}{22}$

Page 44

D.
1. $\frac{1}{12}$
2. $\frac{5}{12}$
3. $\frac{4}{10}$
4. $\frac{6}{21}$
5. $\frac{1}{16}$
6. $\frac{1}{6}$
7. $\frac{2}{60}$
8. $\frac{5}{18}$
9. $\frac{2}{35}$
10. $\frac{1}{26}$
11. $\frac{3}{30}$
12. $\frac{2}{6}$
13. $\frac{15}{24}$
14. $\frac{4}{15}$
15. $\frac{15}{60}$
16. $\frac{6}{40}$
17. $\frac{28}{40}$

18. $\frac{1}{8}$
19. $\frac{18}{25}$
20. $\frac{3}{24}$
21. $\frac{1}{64}$
22. $\frac{3}{50}$
23. $\frac{7}{64}$
24. $\frac{3}{32}$

Page 46

A.
1. $1\frac{1}{2}$
2. $3\frac{1}{3}$
3. $2\frac{4}{7}$
4. 4
5. 4
6. 3
7. $\frac{1}{3}$
8. $3\frac{3}{7}$
9. $\frac{10}{11}$
10. 2
11. 6
12. 2
13. 4
14. 15
15. 8
16. $6\frac{2}{5}$
17. $7\frac{1}{2}$
18. $6\frac{2}{3}$
19. $3\frac{1}{4}$
20. $1\frac{5}{7}$
21. $\frac{7}{8}$
22. $11\frac{1}{7}$
23. $\frac{5}{12}$
24. 7

Page 47

B.
1. 30
2. $\frac{1}{2}$
3. $4\frac{1}{2}$
4. $2\frac{2}{3}$
5. 9
6. $2\frac{5}{8}$
7. 3
8. $4\frac{4}{7}$
9. $11\frac{2}{3}$
10. $1\frac{1}{3}$
11. $4\frac{1}{2}$
12. 24
13. 6
14. 30
15. 10
16. $\frac{10}{13}$

17. $5\frac{3}{7}$
18. $1\frac{1}{32}$
19. $3\frac{6}{7}$
20. $1\frac{5}{16}$
21. 3
22. $1\frac{5}{7}$
23. 5
24. $4\frac{1}{16}$

Page 49

A.
1. 14
2. $7\frac{1}{5}$
3. 6
4. 8
5. $\frac{1}{8}$
6. $\frac{5}{16}$
7. $\frac{1}{10}$
8. 12
9. $\frac{5}{32}$
10. 10
11. $\frac{1}{36}$
12. 16
13. 12
14. $\frac{4}{15}$
15. 5
16. $7\frac{1}{2}$
17. $9\frac{3}{8}$
18. $\frac{1}{15}$
19. $\frac{1}{32}$
20. 18
21. $\frac{4}{25}$
22. $\frac{6}{11}$
23. $\frac{1}{4}$
24. $20\frac{5}{6}$

Page 50

B.
1. 3
2. $\frac{5}{28}$
3. $\frac{5}{9}$
4. 42
5. $5\frac{1}{3}$
6. $1\frac{1}{8}$
7. $\frac{4}{7}$
8. 5
9. 35
10. $1\frac{3}{5}$
11. 36
12. $\frac{7}{128}$
13. $1\frac{2}{3}$
14. 2
15. $\frac{1}{2}$

16. $3\frac{1}{3}$
17. $\frac{10}{27}$
18. 3
19. $\frac{1}{5}$
20. $\frac{2}{3}$
21. 1
22. 18
23. $\frac{3}{338}$
24. $6\frac{3}{4}$

Page 51

C.
1. $\frac{36}{5}$
2. $\frac{7}{4}$
3. $\frac{31}{6}$
4. $\frac{73}{8}$
5. $\frac{51}{5}$
6. $\frac{17}{2}$
7. $\frac{11}{5}$
8. $\frac{35}{8}$
9. $\frac{53}{6}$
10. $\frac{49}{4}$
11. $\frac{27}{7}$
12. $\frac{8}{3}$
13. $\frac{59}{9}$
14. $\frac{31}{4}$
15. $\frac{41}{13}$
16. $\frac{16}{3}$
17. $\frac{43}{6}$
18. $\frac{57}{8}$
19. $\frac{17}{7}$
20. $\frac{25}{12}$
21. $\frac{38}{9}$
22. $\frac{45}{4}$
23. $\frac{31}{16}$
24. $\frac{53}{8}$
25. $\frac{33}{2}$
26. $\frac{43}{32}$
27. $\frac{49}{11}$
28. $\frac{29}{9}$
29. $\frac{27}{5}$
30. $\frac{49}{6}$
31. $\frac{25}{2}$
32. $\frac{32}{3}$
33. $\frac{73}{9}$
34. $\frac{42}{5}$
35. $\frac{46}{15}$
36. $\frac{20}{3}$
37. $\frac{47}{5}$
38. $\frac{13}{4}$
39. $\frac{47}{8}$
40. $\frac{73}{10}$
41. $\frac{27}{4}$

42. $\frac{35}{2}$
43. $\frac{40}{3}$
44. $\frac{19}{7}$
45. $\frac{37}{6}$

Page 53
A.
1. $21\frac{1}{3}$
2. 3
3. $1\frac{2}{9}$
4. 10
5. $6\frac{3}{8}$
6. $2\frac{7}{10}$
7. $9\frac{4}{9}$
8. 27
9. $7\frac{1}{2}$
10. $9\frac{5}{8}$
11. $31\frac{1}{9}$
12. $1\frac{17}{60}$
13. $3\frac{1}{9}$
14. $4\frac{3}{5}$
15. $7\frac{1}{3}$
16. $17\frac{1}{4}$

Page 54
B.
1. 14
2. $12\frac{4}{7}$
3. $\frac{7}{16}$
4. 15
5. $1\frac{1}{20}$
6. 14
7. 6
8. $8\frac{2}{3}$
9. 20
10. 2
C.
1. 1
2. $8\frac{4}{5}$
3. $26\frac{2}{3}$
4. 105
5. $6\frac{8}{9}$
6. 15
7. $\frac{4}{5}$
8. $18\frac{2}{5}$
9. 20
10. 10

Page 55
1. $1\frac{1}{2}$
2. $2\frac{4}{5}$
3. $7\frac{1}{8}$
4. $8\frac{3}{4}$

5. $\frac{3}{16}$
6. $8\frac{3}{4}$
7. $25\frac{1}{3}$
8. $30\frac{1}{4}$
9. 30
10. 6
11. $\frac{12}{35}$
12. $6\frac{7}{8}$
13. $2\frac{3}{4}$
14. 40
15. $\frac{3}{20}$
16. $2\frac{13}{16}$

Page 57
A.
1. $1\frac{1}{20}$
2. $\frac{5}{8}$
3. $2\frac{1}{2}$
4. $1\frac{1}{5}$
5. $\frac{2}{3}$
6. $5\frac{4}{9}$
7. $\frac{9}{22}$
8. 3
9. $1\frac{3}{4}$
10. $\frac{5}{9}$
11. $2\frac{4}{5}$
12. $\frac{1}{5}$

Page 58
B.
1. 1
2. $\frac{15}{16}$
3. $\frac{5}{6}$
4. $1\frac{1}{3}$
5. $\frac{15}{16}$
6. $1\frac{1}{6}$
7. $1\frac{1}{21}$
8. $1\frac{1}{4}$
9. $\frac{4}{5}$
10. $\frac{3}{4}$
11. $1\frac{4}{5}$
12. $2\frac{1}{2}$
13. $\frac{1}{3}$
14. $\frac{1}{8}$
15. $1\frac{1}{5}$
16. 2

Page 59
C.
1. $2\frac{3}{16}$
2. $4\frac{1}{6}$
3. $2\frac{1}{4}$
4. $\frac{4}{5}$

5. 4
6. $2\frac{7}{9}$
7. $3\frac{1}{16}$
8. $1\frac{1}{4}$
9. $\frac{16}{35}$
10. $\frac{24}{25}$
11. $\frac{25}{48}$
12. $2\frac{1}{2}$
13. $1\frac{1}{2}$
14. $1\frac{1}{6}$
15. $1\frac{1}{7}$
16. 2

Page 60
D.
1. $\frac{5}{8}$
2. $\frac{2}{5}$
3. 3
4. $\frac{3}{8}$
5. $1\frac{1}{9}$
6. $2\frac{10}{11}$
7. $\frac{4}{5}$
8. $7\frac{7}{8}$
9. $\frac{1}{3}$
10. $\frac{5}{7}$
11. $\frac{24}{35}$
12. $1\frac{1}{2}$
13. 12
14. $2\frac{2}{3}$
15. $1\frac{2}{3}$
16. $1\frac{3}{8}$
17. $\frac{2}{3}$
18. $\frac{1}{6}$
19. $\frac{5}{6}$
20. $\frac{14}{15}$

Page 62
A.
1. $\frac{1}{12}$
2. 12
3. $\frac{3}{40}$
4. 24
5. $\frac{7}{60}$
6. $23\frac{1}{3}$
B.
1. 45
2. $7\frac{1}{2}$
3. $\frac{3}{16}$
4. 30
5. $\frac{1}{45}$
6. $13\frac{5}{7}$
7. $21\frac{1}{3}$
8. $\frac{3}{50}$

Page 63
C.
1. 20
2. 50
3. 32
4. $\frac{1}{10}$
5. 12
6. $\frac{7}{30}$
7. 12
8. $\frac{2}{25}$
9. $\frac{4}{15}$
10. $14\frac{6}{7}$
11. 25
12. $\frac{1}{25}$
13. $\frac{1}{8}$
14. $5\frac{1}{3}$
15. $\frac{9}{32}$
16. $\frac{3}{20}$
17. $2\frac{2}{15}$
18. 8
19. $\frac{9}{40}$
20. $4\frac{4}{9}$

Pages 64–65
D.
1. $12\frac{1}{2}$
2. $\frac{1}{3}$
3. $\frac{5}{24}$
4. 27
5. $\frac{1}{16}$
6. $11\frac{2}{3}$
7. 16
8. 16
9. 10
10. $\frac{1}{10}$
11. $\frac{1}{25}$
12. 48
13. 8
14. $10\frac{2}{3}$
15. $\frac{2}{9}$
16. $16\frac{1}{3}$
17. $\frac{1}{32}$
18. $\frac{7}{24}$
19. 6
20. $\frac{7}{32}$
E.
1. 3
2. 60
3. $\frac{1}{36}$
4. $\frac{3}{16}$
5. 14
6. 15
7. $\frac{1}{36}$

8. $\frac{1}{6}$
9. $8\frac{1}{3}$
10. $1\frac{1}{3}$
11. $\frac{3}{16}$
12. 2
13. 12
14. $4\frac{4}{5}$
15. $\frac{5}{18}$
16. 56
17. 16
18. $\frac{1}{60}$
19. 16
20. $\frac{7}{9}$
21. $\frac{1}{6}$
22. $\frac{3}{16}$
23. $\frac{1}{8}$
24. $9\frac{1}{7}$
25. $\frac{5}{32}$
26. $\frac{1}{12}$
27. $\frac{1}{27}$
28. $\frac{1}{24}$
29. $\frac{1}{24}$
30. $\frac{1}{12}$

Page 67
A.
1. $1\frac{5}{9}$
2. 2
3. $6\frac{1}{4}$
4. $\frac{1}{10}$
5. $\frac{16}{25}$
6. $1\frac{9}{16}$
7. $1\frac{1}{20}$
8. $2\frac{3}{5}$

Page 68
B.
1. 6
2. $4\frac{2}{9}$
3. $5\frac{5}{7}$
4. 2
5. 3
6. $2\frac{6}{7}$
7. 2
8. 2
9. 6
10. 42

Page 69
C.
1. $2\frac{1}{3}$
2. $\frac{5}{13}$
3. $\frac{11}{16}$
4. $1\frac{2}{9}$
5. 6
6. $\frac{17}{40}$
7. $\frac{1}{4}$
8. $2\frac{6}{17}$
9. $1\frac{1}{2}$
10. $\frac{11}{24}$

Page 70
1. 2
2. $\frac{1}{5}$
3. $\frac{1}{36}$
4. $\frac{1}{2}$
5. $1\frac{1}{20}$
6. $15\frac{3}{4}$
7. $\frac{2}{15}$
8. $1\frac{23}{75}$
9. $5\frac{5}{7}$
10. 21
11. $\frac{1}{30}$
12. 30

Page 72
A.
1. .50
2. .40
3. .25
4. .125
5. .1666
6. .75
7. .3333
8. .375
9. .60
10. .4166
11. .10
12. .1875
13. .05
14. .7142
15. .60
16. .2222
17. .1818
18. .4375
19. .1333
20. .8888

Page 73
B.
1. .80
2. .0833
3. .8333
4. .875
5. .1052
6. .4545
7. .4166
8. .70
9. .1428
10. .7777
11. .20
12. .625
13. .8571
14. .8181
15. .0625
16. .4666
17. .4166
18. .1538
19. .1363
20. .16

Page 74
1.	50%	63%	48%	99%
2.	80%	5%	40%	20%
3.	110%	40%	101%	60%
4.	90%	203%	75%	55%
5.	308%	425%	4%	170%
6.	70%	12%	68%	17.5%
7.	18.75%	62.5%	43.75%	33.33%

Page 75
| 1. | .25 | .03 | .72 | .82 |
| 2. | .08 | .75 | .11 | .63 |

| 3. | .015 | .042 | .0766 | .1616 |
| 4. | .0333 | .1875 | .0683 | .4066 |

Page 78
A.
1. $.80
2. $.52
3. $.21
4. $.83
5. $.06
6. $.09
7. $.39
8. $1.98

Page 79
B.
1. $4.02	2. $2.20	3. $2.44
4. $.07	5. $1.50	6. $20.62
7. $6.67	8. $6.65	9. $0.17
10. $.23	11. $2.56	12. $.41
13. $.93	14. $1.91	15. $5.75

Page 80
C.
1. $1.85	2. $95.80	3. $1.60
4. $1.30	5. $.62	6. $3.19
7. $1.65	8. $13.33	9. $1.17
10. $1.50	11. $112.00	12. $0.84
13. $.44	14. $29.96	15. $1.25
16. $1.00	17. $1.35	18. $3.75

Page 82
A.
1. $.67
2. $1.92
3. $.57
4. $8.23
5. $8.72

Page 83
B.
1. $2.12
2. $4.35
3. $1.20
4. $2.39
5. $2.99
6. $7.50

Page 84
C.
1. $81.25
2. $8.12
3. $74.53

4. $31.30
5. $11.49
6. $1.26
7. $9.50
8. $29.00
9. $5.50
10. $1.31

Page 85
D.
1. $37.39
2. $.67
3. $3.60
4. $1.85
5. $2.44
6. $9.74
7. $3.06
8. $.61
9. $1.14
10. $1.47

Page 87
A.
1. $.15; .25; .50; .75; 1.00
2. $.50; .75; 1.00
3. $.08; .09; .10; .15; .25; .50; .75; 1.00
4. $.78; .79; .80; .90; 1.00
5. $.29; .30; .40; .50; 1.00
6. $.50; .75; 1.00
7. $.33; .34; .35; .40; .50; .75; 1.00
8. $.64; .65; .75; 1.00
9. $.72; .73; .74; .75; 1.00
10. $.50; .75; 1.00
11. $.23; .24; .25; .50; .75; 1.00
12. $.25; .50; 1.00

Page 88
B.
1. $.19; .20; .25; .50; 1.00
2. $.28; .29; .30; .40; .50; .75; 1.00
3. $.67; .68; .69; .70; .75; 1.00
4. $.30; .40; .50; .75; 1.00
5. $.47; .48; .49; .50; 1.00
6. $.25; .50; 1.00
7. $.50; .75; 1.00
8. $.43; .44; .45; .50; .75; 1.00
9. $.25; .50; .75; 1.00
10. $.65; .75; 1.00
11. $.24; .25; .50; 1.00
12. $.80; .90; 1.00

Page 89

	$.01	$.05	$.10	$.25	$.50	$ Change
1.				3		$.75
2.	3		1		1	$.63
3.	4				1	$.54
4.	2	1		1		$.32
5.	1	1		1	1	$.81
6.	2	1	1		1	$.67
7.	1		2			$.21
8.	2		2			$.22
9.	4		1		1	$.64
10.	3		2		1	$.73
11.	1		1	1	1	$.86
12.		1	1	1		$.40
13.	4		2		1	$.74
14.	2	1	1	1	1	$.92
15.	2	1			1	$.57
16.	2	1				$.12
17.				1		$.25
18.	4		1	1		$.39
19.	1		2		1	$.61
20.	4	1		1		$.34

Page 90

	$.01	$.05	$.10	$.25	$.50	$ Change
1.	3	1	1	1		$.43
2.	3				1	$.53
3.	2		2	1		$.47
4.	4	1				$.09
5.	4					$.04
6.	1					$.01
7.	1	1				$.06
8.	4					$.04
9.	3		1			$.13
10.	3		2			$.23
11.	1	1		1		$.31
12.	3			1	1	$.78
13.		1				$.05
14.	4			1		$.29
15.	2	1				$.07
16.	4		1			$.14
17.	3	1				$.08
18.	1		1			$.11
19.	4	1	1			$.19
20.			2			$.20

Page 91

A.
1. 6
2. $15\frac{19}{20}$
3. $12\frac{1}{4}$
4. $5\frac{13}{24}$
5. $7\frac{17}{18}$
6. $10\frac{1}{2}$
7. $9\frac{1}{5}$
8. $12\frac{5}{18}$
9. $11\frac{7}{8}$

B.
1. $\frac{1}{5}$
2. $1\frac{7}{15}$
3. $34\frac{9}{10}$
4. $7\frac{15}{16}$
5. $4\frac{1}{20}$
6. $1\frac{23}{24}$
7. $\frac{11}{35}$
8. $14\frac{7}{8}$
9. $9\frac{19}{20}$

Page 92

C.
1. 10
2. 25
3. $1\frac{17}{32}$
4. $27\frac{1}{2}$
5. 33
6. $3\frac{1}{30}$
7. 16
8. $\frac{17}{28}$
9. $19\frac{4}{5}$
10. $3\frac{1}{2}$
11. $14\frac{2}{3}$
12. $7\frac{1}{2}$

D.
1. $\frac{1}{5}$
2. 16
3. $\frac{5}{6}$
4. 6
5. 31
6. $\frac{10}{17}$
7. $\frac{11}{12}$
8. $2\frac{1}{2}$
9. 4
10. $\frac{5}{26}$
11. $1\frac{11}{14}$
12. $1\frac{3}{10}$

Page 93

E.
1. .04
2. .25
3. .18
4. .03
5. .025
6. .40
7. .35
8. .0325
9. .333
10. .50
11. .075
12. .0875
13. .035
14. .0775
15. .08125
16. .09625
17. .1175
18. .065
19. .605
20. .1166
21. .333
22. .0516
23. .13375
24. .185
25. .175
26. .091818
27. .0316
28. 1.05
29. 2.6
30. 1.14

USING FRACTIONS

F.

1. $\frac{4}{3}$
2. $\frac{7}{2}$
3. $\frac{7}{4}$
4. $\frac{35}{8}$
5. $\frac{11}{5}$
6. $\frac{42}{5}$
7. $\frac{10}{7}$
8. $\frac{32}{3}$
9. $\frac{33}{7}$
10. $\frac{34}{5}$
11. $\frac{31}{8}$
12. $\frac{31}{6}$
13. $\frac{13}{2}$
14. $\frac{19}{16}$
15. $\frac{48}{5}$
16. $\frac{32}{5}$
17. $\frac{73}{10}$
18. $\frac{31}{9}$
19. $\frac{9}{4}$
20. $\frac{7}{3}$
21. $\frac{15}{4}$
22. $\frac{34}{5}$
23. $\frac{23}{6}$
24. $\frac{41}{4}$
25. $\frac{28}{3}$
26. $\frac{66}{7}$
27. $\frac{17}{4}$
28. $\frac{64}{9}$

J.

	$.01	$.05	$.10	$.25	$.50	Change
1.	2		2	1	1	$.97
2.	3	1		1		$.33
3.			1	1	1	$.85
4.	2					$.02
5.	3	1	1	1	1	$.93
6.	2	1				$.07
7.	3		2			$.23
8.	1	1		1		$.31
9.	2	1		1	1	$.82
10.	2		1			$.12

Page 94

G.

1. $.28
2. $.29
3. $1.49
4. $1.13
5. $.07
6. $1.30
7. $.18
8. $.30
9. $2.90
10. $2.22
11. $2.54
12. $1.33
13. $.71
14. $.14
15. $.10
16. $2.36

H.

1. 5
2. $5\frac{1}{2}$
3. 12
4. 8
5. 3
6. $12\frac{1}{8}$
7. $1\frac{3}{4}$
8. $3\frac{1}{3}$
9. 7
10. $1\frac{4}{5}$
11. $3\frac{1}{3}$
12. $4\frac{10}{11}$
13. $4\frac{1}{3}$
14. 4
15. $1\frac{2}{3}$
16. $2\frac{1}{10}$
17. 4
18. $6\frac{1}{2}$
19. $7\frac{1}{2}$
20. $5\frac{2}{3}$
21. $2\frac{5}{6}$
22. $3\frac{1}{7}$
23. $2\frac{1}{9}$
24. $1\frac{7}{12}$

Pages 95–96

I.

1. $\frac{5}{6}$ yd.
2. $20.52
3. $1.60
4. $5.94
5. $1.49
6. 2
7. $39.84
8. $8.33
9. 3
10. $11.25
11. $10.50
12. $31.50

Using Money

Page 6
1. 5 pennies
2. 10 pennies
   2 nickels
3. 25 pennies
   5 nickels
   2 dimes and 1 nickel
4. 50 pennies
   10 nickels
   5 dimes
   2 quarters

Page 8
1. 100, 20, 10, 4, 2
2. 100, 50, 20, 10, 5
3. 100, 50, 10, 5, 2, 1
4. 200, 100, 40, 20, 10, 2
5. 40, 20, 4, 2
6. 100, 20, 10, 5

Page 9

Dollar Sign	Decimal Point	Dimes	Pennies	Amount of Money
$	.	4	5	$.45
$	.	1	9	$.19
$	.	7	6	$.76
$	.	3	3	$.33
$	.	9	8	$.98

Page 10

Dollar Sign	One Hundred Dollars	Ten Dollars	One Dollar	.	Dimes	Pennies
$			9	.	5	2
$		1	7	.	9	3
$		3	0	.	4	0
$		1	4	.	9	3
$		5	7	.	8	5
$	1	5	0	.	1	0
$	4	0	2	.	8	0
$	1	1	2	.	1	7
$	5	3	3	.	0	4
$	7	6	2	.	0	0

Page 11
1. $.51
2. $.62
3. $.50
4. $.52
5. $.48
6. $.25

Page 12
1. $.40
2. $.25
3. $2.25
4. $.60
5. $1.00
6. $1.30
7. $.55
8. $3.50
9. $.99
10. $2.50
11. $1.50
12. $2.50
13. $9.00
14. $25.00
15. $80.00
16. $40.00
17. $40.00
18. $29.00
19. $45.00
20. $70.00
21. $80.00
22. $30.00
23. $2.84
24. $17.45
25. $80.19
26. $51.05
27. $150.42
28. $74.36

Page 13
1. B
2. E
3. A
4. D
5. C

Page 14
1. B
2. D
3. E
4. C
5. A

Page 15
1. $40.00
2. $40.00
3. $36.00

Page 16
1. $100.00
2. $27.00
3. $25.00

Page 17
1. E
2. D
3. A
4. C
5. B

Page 18
1. C
2. D
3. B
4. E
5. A

Page 19
1. $6.75
2. $11.25
3. $7.08

Page 20

Number of Coins	Pennies	Nickels	Dimes	Quarters	Half-Dollars
1	$.01	$.05	$.10	$.25	$.50
2	$.02	$.10	$.20	$.50	$1.00
3	$.03	$.15	$.30	$.75	$1.50
4	$.04	$.20	$.40	$1.00	$2.00
5	$.05	$.25	$.50	$1.25	$2.50
6	$.06	$.30	$.60	$1.50	$3.00
7	$.07	$.35	$.70	$1.75	$3.50
8	$.08	$.40	$.80	$2.00	$4.00
9	$.09	$.45	$.90	$2.25	$4.50
10	$.10	$.50	$1.00	$2.50	$5.00
11	$.11	$.55	$1.10	$2.75	$5.50
12	$.12	$.60	$1.20	$3.00	$6.00
13	$.13	$.65	$1.30	$3.25	$6.50
14	$.14	$.70	$1.40	$3.50	$7.00
15	$.15	$.75	$1.50	$3.75	$7.50
16	$.16	$.80	$1.60	$4.00	$8.00
17	$.17	$.85	$1.70	$4.25	$8.50
18	$.18	$.90	$1.80	$4.50	$9.00
19	$.19	$.95	$1.90	$4.75	$9.50
20	$.20	$1.00	$2.00	$5.00	$10.00

Page 21

Number of Coins	One-Dollar Bill(s)	Five-Dollar Bill(s)	Ten-Dollar Bill(s)	Twenty-Dollar Bill(s)	Fifty-Dollar Bill(s)	One Hundred-Dollar Bill(s)
1	$1.00	$5.00	$10.00	$20.00	$50.00	$100.00
2	$2.00	$10.00	$20.00	$40.00	$100.00	$200.00
3	$3.00	$15.00	$30.00	$60.00	$150.00	$300.00
4	$4.00	$20.00	$40.00	$80.00	$200.00	$400.00
5	$5.00	$25.00	$50.00	$100.00	$250.00	$500.00
6	$6.00	$30.00	$60.00	$120.00	$300.00	$600.00
7	$7.00	$35.00	$70.00	$140.00	$350.00	$700.00
8	$8.00	$40.00	$80.00	$160.00	$400.00	$800.00
9	$9.00	$45.00	$90.00	$180.00	$450.00	$900.00
10	$10.00	$50.00	$100.00	$200.00	$500.00	$1,000.00
11	$11.00	$55.00	$110.00	$220.00	$550.00	$1,100.00
12	$12.00	$60.00	$120.00	$240.00	$600.00	$1,200.00
13	$13.00	$65.00	$130.00	$260.00	$650.00	$1,300.00
14	$14.00	$70.00	$140.00	$280.00	$700.00	$1,400.00
15	$15.00	$75.00	$150.00	$300.00	$750.00	$1,500.00
16	$16.00	$80.00	$160.00	$320.00	$800.00	$1,600.00
17	$17.00	$85.00	$170.00	$340.00	$850.00	$1,700.00
18	$18.00	$90.00	$180.00	$360.00	$900.00	$1,800.00
19	$19.00	$95.00	$190.00	$380.00	$950.00	$1,900.00
20	$20.00	$100.00	$200.00	$400.00	$1,000.00	$2,000.00

Page 22
1. $.30
2. $.50
3. $.30
4. $.29
5. $.75
6. $.40
7. $.35
8. $.25
9. $1.00
10. $.45
11. $1.25
12. $1.00
13. $.90
14. $1.00
15. $1.70
16. $1.00
17. $1.75
18. $.75
19. $3.00
20. $.60
21. $.70
22. $.55
23. $1.50
24. $.80
25. $.51
26. $2.00
27. $1.50
28. $.70
29. $2.00
30. $2.25

Page 23
1. 12
2. 20
3. 500
4. 5
5. 19
6. 21
7. 15
8. 6
9. 80
10. 30
11. 11
12. 9
13. 40
14. 20
15. 39
16. 16
17. 40
18. 120
19. 38
20. 67

Page 24
1. $.28
2. $.22
3. $.40
4. $.90
5. $.45
6. $.23
7. $.75
8. $.60
9. $.55
10. $.75
11. $.65
12. $1.25
13. $.75
14. $1.50
15. $1.10
16. $1.10

Page 25
1. 2 dimes, 1 nickel
2. 3 dimes
3. 4 nickels
4. 1 quarter, 1 dime
5. 4 quarters
6. 1 dime, 1 nickel
7. 1 quarter, 2 dimes
8. 3 dimes, 2 nickels
9. 1 quarter, 1 dime, 1 nickel
10. 2 half-dollars
11. 3 quarters
12. 1 nickel, 5 pennies
13. 1 quarter, 1 nickel
14. 2 nickels, 5 pennies
15. 5 nickels
16. 1 half-dollar, 1 nickel

Page 26
Answers will vary but may include the following:
2. 1 quarter; 2 dimes, 1 nickel

3. 3 quarters, 1 dime, 1 penny; 8 dimes, 1 nickel, 1 penny
4. 2 quarters; 5 dimes
5. 3 quarters, 2 dimes; 9 dimes, 1 nickel
6. 1 quarter, 1 dime, 2 pennies; 3 dimes, 1 nickel, 2 pennies
7. 2 quarters, 2 dimes, 1 penny; 7 dimes, 1 penny
8. 1 quarter, 2 dimes, 3 pennies; 4 dimes, 1 nickel, 3 pennies
9. 1 one-dollar bill, 1 nickel, 1 penny; 4 quarters, 1 nickel, 1 penny
10. 1 dime, 2 pennies; 2 nickels, 2 pennies
11. 1 nickel; 5 pennies
12. 1 quarter, 1 dime, 1 nickel, 2 pennies; 4 dimes, 2 pennies
13. 1 twenty-dollar bill, 2 quarters; 2 ten-dollar bills, 2 quarters
14. 1 ten-dollar bill, 1 five-dollar bill, 2 quarters, 1 penny; 3 five-dollar bills, 2 quarters, 1 penny
15. 1 five-dollar bill, 1 quarter; five one-dollar bills, 1 quarter
16. 1 ten-dollar bill, 1 one-dollar bill; 2 five-dollar bills, 1 one-dollar bill
17. 1 one-dollar bill, 2 quarters; 6 quarters
18. 4 twenty-dollar bills, 1 five-dollar bill; 8 ten-dollar bills, 1 five-dollar bill
19. 3 quarters, 1 dime, 1 nickel; 9 dimes
20. 1 five-dollar bill, 3 one-dollar bills, 1 nickel; 8 one-dollar bills, 1 nickel

Page 27
1. $5.40
2. $10.25
3. $5.50
4. $20.50
5. $10.75
6. $2.75
7. $4.30
8. $10.55
9. $11.50
10. $25.25
11. $15.50
12. $6.30

Page 28
1. $24.15
2. $50.75
3. $15.63
4. $60.75

USING MONEY

Page 29

5. $.60	**19.** $90.00
6. $.20	**20.** $20.00
7. $1.25	**21.** $30.00
8. $.80	**22.** $19.00
9. $2.00	**23.** $50.00
10. $.25	**24.** $50.00
11 $1.50	**25.** $60.00
12. $.50	**26.** $80.00
13. $3.00	**27.** $5.37
14. $.88	**28.** $8.55
15. $2.00	**29.** $15.60
16. $.75	**30.** $90.18
17. $8.00	**31.** $41.09
18. $60.00	**32.** $275.66

Page 31

1. $.50	**2.** $.79	**3.** $.46	**4.** $.77	**5.** $.99
6. $.49	**7.** $.80	**8.** $.85	**9.** $.90	**10.** $.68
11. $1.59	**12.** $1.06	**13.** $2.01	**14.** $1.58	**15.** $1.78
16. $1.39	**17.** $1.48	**18.** $1.42	**19.** $1.07	**20.** $1.80
21. $1.43	**22.** $1.59	**23.** $1.83	**24.** $1.20	**25.** $1.25
26. $.90	**27.** $1.68	**28.** $.52	**29.** $2.02	**30.** $2.28

Page 32

1. $2.83	**2.** $4.65	**3.** $8.63	**4.** $2.49	**5.** $4.77
6. $2.77	**7.** $3.53	**8.** $7.43	**9.** $4.77	**10.** $5.34
11. $5.82	**12.** $3.22	**13.** $2.84	**14.** $3.84	**15.** $4.82
16. $13.41	**17.** $9.34	**18.** $15.58	**19.** $13.53	**20.** $11.64
21. $14.94				
22. $9.87				

Page 33

1. $25.67	**2.** $47.48	**3.** $19.65	**4.** $65.66	**5.** $74.85
6. $35.74	**7.** $35.82	**8.** $66.66	**9.** $74.67	**10.** $83.87
11. $27.16	**12.** $49.45	**13.** $67.21	**14.** $87.51	**15.** $56.45
16. $50.44	**17.** $30.58	**18.** $40.50	**19.** $92.65	**20.** $49.19
21. $120.07	**22.** $49.80	**23.** $96.33	**24.** $116.86	**25.** $136.74
26. $58.95	**27.** $96.37	**28.** $200.50	**29.** $119.51	**30.** $126.84

Page 34

1. $180.83	**2.** $258.76	**3.** $549.94	**4.** $595.93
5. $697.89	**6.** $274.78	**7.** $687.94	**8.** $384.84
9. $498.69	**10.** $948.96	**11.** $377.35	**12.** $197.86
13. $696.79	**14.** $497.60	**15.** $988.84	**16.** $385.62
17. $869.00	**18.** $495.17	**19.** $953.32	**20.** $768.44
21. $651.91			
22. $1,242.93			

Page 35

1. $.89
2. $18.64
3. $2.21
4. $9.51
5. $5.85
6. $7.90

Page 36

7. $5.86
8. $4.62
9. $8.39
10. $18.70
11. $65.76
12. $85.32

Page 37

1. $2.73	**2.** $.41	**3.** $4.33	**4.** $2.02	**5.** $4.76
6. $3.22	**7.** $6.03	**8.** $2.50	**9.** $5.25	**10.** $8.02
11. $4.05	**12.** $1.12	**13.** $3.48	**14.** $1.59	**15.** $3.48
16. $7.82	**17.** $1.85	**18.** $.55	**19.** $1.24	**20.** $.34
21. $6.22				
22. $.79				

Page 38

1. $22.03	**2.** $17.33	**3.** $54.06	**4.** $4.33	**5.** $30.45
6. $33.04	**7.** $82.57	**8.** $50.46	**9.** $24.63	**10.** $64.64
11. $5.58	**12.** $32.31	**13.** $23.08	**14.** $41.58	**15.** $18.09
16. $20.52	**17.** $14.35	**18.** $43.94	**19.** $40.90	**20.** $40.66
21. $45.22	**22.** $8.14	**23.** $28.91	**24.** $18.13	**25.** $32.22
26. $3.76	**27.** $18.74	**28.** $38.49	**29.** $56.29	**30.** $7.47

Page 39

1. $154.01	**2.** $272.79	**3.** $61.63	**4.** $814.46	**5.** $271.12
6. $471.18	**7.** $110.17	**8.** $146.23	**9.** $73.07	**10.** $212.28
11. $110.58	**12.** $241.16	**13.** $190.82	**14.** $103.05	**15.** $143.63
16. $314.65	**17.** $224.74	**18.** $106.17	**19.** $244.11	**20.** $355.56
21. $58.76	**22.** $276.22	**23.** $288.77	**24.** $703.88	**25.** $52.56
26. $211.09				
27. $401.16				
28. $39.15				

Page 40

1. $541.69
2. $53.68
3. $17.18
4. $14.74

Page 41

5. $592.84
6. $1,884.25
7. $5.16
8. $238.65
9. $135.07
10. $251.03

Page 42

1. $1.03
2. $4.18
3. $4.29
4. $22.41
5. $1.62
6. $22.27

Page 43
7. $102.43
8. $333.08
9. $253.56
10. $218.19
11. $488.28
12. $202.15

Page 44
13. $1,310.13
14. $6,343.02
15. $4,160.35
16. $3,314.47
17. $5,355.52
18. $2,668.46

Page 45

1. $2.24	2. $.90	3. $.82	4. $.39	5. $.84
6. $.75	7. $.75	8. $.34	9. $.87	10. $.76
11. $2.05	12. $7.20	13. $1.56	14. $1.44	15. $3.00
16. $1.70	17. $3.40	18. $3.68	19. $4.41	20. $5.70
21. $.65	22. $1.60	23. $5.94	24. $.96	25. $3.60
26. $1.00	27. $.90	28. $.84	29. $4.25	30. $2.10

Page 46

1. $3.09	2. $4.86	3. $8.06	4. $8.44	5. $9.60
6. $6.57	7. $2.56	8. $9.15	9. $8.50	10. $9.72
11. $9.72	12. $7.18	13. $5.28	14. $5.40	15. $8.25
16. $23.55	17. $32.30	18. $17.88	19. $52.50	20. $78.72
21. $10.04	22. $19.20	23. $16.46	24. $47.16	25. $45.72
26. $15.20	27. $33.00	28. $36.60	29. $48.65	30. $14.28

Page 47

31. $24.82	32. $60.93	33. $28.46	34. $44.80	35. $90.60
36. $56.32	37. $50.75	38. $160.60	39. $96.51	40. $46.98
41. $98.82	42. $87.00	43. $25.30	44. $52.30	45. $83.74
46. $91.52	47. $86.70	48. $92.96	49. $83.65	50. $80.82
51. $417.30	52. $263.36	53. $120.82	54. $119.90	55. $194.58
56. $67.68	57. $84.18	58. $177.25	59. $70.12	60. $211.12

Page 48

61. $224.68	62. $606.93	63. $575.50	64. $880.84
65. $848.20	66. $939.72	67. $707.42	68. $862.58
69. $338.94	70. $806.96	71. $641.30	72. $508.60
73. $411.94	74. $594.15	75. $950.25	76. $819.36
77. $1,135.40			
78. $3,457.50			

Page 49

1. $2.40	2. $2.99	3. $8.61	4. $6.05
5. $3.64	6. $2.70	7. $5.52	8. $4.32
9. $16.10	10. $30.74	11. $22.78	12. $17.38
13. $4.80	14. $4.60	15. $8.00	16. $9.90
17. $4.50	18. $5.70	19. $6.50	20. $9.00
21. $10.35	22. $2.70	23. $5.32	24. $4.84

Page 50

25. $38.34	26. $56.25
27. $249.48	28. $173.43
29. $101.91	30. $236.08
31. $192.28	32. $450.45
33. $312.12	34. $98.67
35. $439.11	36. $122.92
37. $220.08	38. $394.24
39. $283.62	40. $453.60
41. $8,006.18	42. $41.20

Page 51

1. $.60	2. $.75	3. $.84	4. $5.10	5. $5.68
6. $8.82	7. $9.06	8. $7.63	9. $5.92	10. $63.84
11. $51.00	12. $54.63	13. $84.60	14. $64.98	15. $55.95
16. $342.72	17. $665.52	18. $386.34	19. $74.26	20. $78.60

Page 52

1. $347.20	2. $574.49	3. $910.02	4. $527.56
5. $1,340.88	6. $1,827.84	7. $1,218.28	8. $2,646.00
9. $3,512.78	10. $3,123.38	11. $2,439.84	12. $2,560.04
13. $4,371.92	14. $2,035.41	15. $2,424.00	16. $9,048.96

Page 53

1. $.04	2. $.03	3. $.01	4. $.02
5. $.04	6. $.08	7. $.06	8. $.08
9. $.41	10. $.12	11. $.10	12. $.12
13. $.14	14. $.17	15. $.12	16. $.14
17. $4.10	18. $3.31	19. $1.20	20. $1.01
21. $.02	22. $.07	23. $.32	24. $.17

Page 54

1. $1.24	2. $2.01	3. $3.24	4. $3.10	5. $4.03
6. $2.80	7. $1.41	8. $2.42	9. $1.53	10. $1.28
11. $1.75	12. $1.33	13. $1.57	14. $1.16	15. $1.85
16. $2.86				
17. $2.23				
18. $2.49				

Page 55

19. $21.10	20. $23.41	21. $20.16	22. $32.10
23. $18.42	24. $14.20	25. $24.32	26. $25.24
27. $15.72	28. $28.95	29. $14.77	30. $14.30
31. $16.89	32. $27.58	33. $15.72	34. $22.56
35. $6.24	36. $3.42	37. $6.85	38. $15.24

Page 56

39. $321.40	40. $312.01	41. $120.12	42. $432.14
43. $152.10	44. $141.21	45. $151.10	46. $484.21
47. $128.21	48. $244.20	49. $395.42	50. $142.10
51. $395.94			
52. $75.40			

Page 57

1. $.03	**2.** $.02	**3.** $.04	**4.** $.04
5. $.76	**6.** $.20	**7.** $.31	**8.** $.35
9. $3.23	**10.** $3.27	**11.** $9.86	**12.** $2.08
13. $24.50	**14.** $38.50	**15.** $19.50	**16.** $15.60
17. $16.00	**18.** $24.00	**19.** $26.00	**20.** $19.00

Page 58

21. $.29		**30.** $1.75	
22. $.38		**31.** $2.50	
23. $.51		**32.** $5.02	
24. $.23		**33.** $3.01	
25. $.52		**34.** $2.02	
26. $1.19		**35.** $16.00	
27. $.99		**36.** $1.13	
28. $.38		**37.** $7.52	
29. $2.05		**38.** $3.95	

Page 59

1. $1.32
2. $1.52
3. $.49
4. $23.84
5. $9.85
6. $275.58

Page 60

1. $1.92	**2.** $3.46	**3.** $1.80	**4.** $1.23	**5.** $1.45
6. $14.97	**7.** $34.89	**8.** $8.49	**9.** $5.42	**10.** $15.52
11. $85.42	**12.** $89.75	**13.** $164.96	**14.** $56.40	**15.** $87.64
16. $5.29	**17.** $3.75	**18.** $2.63	**19.** $1.49	**20.** $5.74
21. $42.50	**22.** $26.80	**23.** $31.50	**24.** $14.60	**25.** $63.60

Page 61

1. It separates dollars from cents.
2. It is placed in front of the first number.
3.
a. $9.76
b. $976
c. $976; The decimal point has been placed after the six, making the amount nine hundred seventy-six dollars.
4. The decimal points must be lined up one under the other.
5. The number of decimal places in the product is equal to the number of decimal places in the multiplicand.
6. It should be placed above the decimal point in the problem.
7.

a. $2.50	**g.** $105.00
b. $250.00	**h.** $1.05
c. $510.00	**i.** $.72
d. $5.10	**j.** $7.02
e. $8.25	**k.** $72.00
f. $825.00	**l.** $702.00

Page 62

1. $59.05	**2.** $62.67	**3.** $119.17	**4.** $440.18	**5.** $1,401.25
6. $233.05	**7.** $644.86	**8.** $407.39	**9.** $728.38	**10.** $554.28
11. $8.04	**12.** $9.72	**13.** $6.75	**14.** $69.36	**15.** $34.00
16. $49.63	**17.** $87.60	**18.** $78.54	**19.** $69.46	**20.** $67.83
21. $194.88	**22.** $848.82	**23.** $4.30	**24.** $3.28	**25.** $1.40
26. $14.76	**27.** $7.59	**28.** $37.50	**29.** $26.75	**30.** $17.50
31. $57.60				
32. $12.50				

Page 63

	1	2	3	4	5	6	7	8	9	10
Pennies	$.01	$.02	$.03	$.04	$.05	$.06	$.07	$.08	$.09	$.10
Nickels	$.05	$.10	$.15	$.20	$.25	$.30	$.35	$.40	$.45	$.50
Dimes	$.10	$.20	$.30	$.40	$.50	$.60	$.70	$.80	$.90	$1.00
Quarters	$.25	$.50	$.75	$1.00	$1.25	$1.50	$1.75	$2.00	$2.25	$2.50
Half-dollars	$.50	$1.00	$1.50	$2.00	$2.50	$3.00	$3.50	$4.00	$4.50	$5.00
One-dollar Bills	$1.00	$2.00	$3.00	$4.00	$5.00	$6.00	$7.00	$8.00	$9.00	$10.00
Five-dollar Bills	$5.00	$10.00	$15.00	$20.00	$25.00	$30.00	$35.00	$40.00	$45.00	$50.00
Ten-dollar Bills	$10.00	$20.00	$30.00	$40.00	$50.00	$60.00	$70.00	$80.00	$90.00	$100.00

Pennies	$.10
Nickels	.50
Dimes	1.00
Quarters	2.50
Half-dollars	5.00
One dollar bills	10.00
Five-dollar bills	50.00
Ten-dollar bills	100.00
Total	$169.10

Page 64

	1	2	3	4	5	6	7	8	9
Pennies	$.01	$.02	$.03	$.04	$.05	$.06	$.07	$.08	$.09
Nickels	$.05	$.10	$.15	$.20	$.25	$.30	$.35	$.40	
Dimes	$.10	$.20	$.30	$.40	$.50	$.60	$.70		
Quarters	$.25	$.50	$.75	$1.00	$1.25	$1.50	$1.75	$2.00	$2.25
Half-dollars	$.50	$1.00	$1.50	$2.00	$2.50				
One-dollar Bills	$1.00	$2.00	$3.00	$4.00	$5.00	$6.00	$7.00		
Five-dollar Bills	$5.00	$10.00	$15.00	$20.00	$25.00	$30.00	$35.00	$40.00	
Ten-dollar Bills	$10.00	$20.00	$30.00	$40.00	$50.00	$60.00			

Pennies	$.09
Nickels	.40
Dimes	.70
Quarters	2.25
Half-dollars	2.50
One-dollar bills	7.00
Five-dollar bills	40.00
Ten-dollar bills	60.00
Total	$112.94

Page 65

	1	2	3	4	5	6	7	8	9
Pennies	$.01	$.02	$.03	$.04	$.05	$.06	$.07	$.08	$.09
Nickels	$.05	$.10	$.15	$.20	$.25	$.30	$.35	$.40	$.45
Dimes	$.10	$.20	$.30	$.40	$.50	$.60	$.70	$.80	$.90
Quarters	$.25	$.50	$.75	$1.00	$1.25	$1.50	$1.75	$2.00	$2.25
Half-dollars	$.50	$1.00	$1.50	$2.00	$2.50	$3.00	$3.50	$4.00	$4.50
One-dollar Bills	$1.00	$2.00	$3.00	$4.00	$5.00	$6.00	$7.00	$8.00	$9.00
Five-dollar Bills	$5.00	$10.00	$15.00	$20.00	$25.00	$30.00	$35.00	$40.00	$45.00
Ten-dollar Bills	$10.00	$20.00	$30.00	$40.00	$50.00	$60.00	$70.00	$80.00	$90.00
Twenty-dollar Bills	$20.00	$40.00	$60.00	$80.00	$100.00	$120.00	$140.00	$160.00	$180.00

Pennies	$.09
Nickels	.45
Dimes	.90
Quarters	2.25
Half-dollars	4.50
One-dollar bills	9.00
Five-dollar bills	45.00
Ten-dollar bills	90.00
Twenty-dollar bills	180.00
Total	$332.19

Page 66

	1	2	3	4	5	6	7	8	9
Pennies	$.01	$.02	$.03	$.04	$.05	$.06	$.07		
Nickels	$.05	$.10	$.15	$.20	$.25	$.30	$.35	$.40	
Dimes	$.10	$.20	$.30	$.40	$.50	$.60	$.70	$.80	$.90
Quarters	$.25	$.50	$.75	$1.00	$1.25	$1.50	$1.75		
Half-dollars	$.50	$1.00	$1.50	$2.00	$2.50	$3.00	$3.50	$4.00	$4.50
One-dollar Bills	$1.00	$2.00	$3.00	$4.00	$5.00	$6.00	$7.00		
Five-dollar Bills	$5.00	$10.00	$15.00	$20.00	$25.00	$30.00	$35.00	$40.00	$45.00
Ten-dollar Bills	$10.00	$20.00	$30.00	$40.00	$50.00	$60.00	$70.00		
Twenty-dollar Bills	$20.00	$40.00	$60.00	$80.00	$100.00	$120.00			

Pennies	$.07
Nickels	.40
Dimes	.90
Quarters	1.75
Half-dollars	4.50
One-dollar bills	7.00
Five-dollar bills	45.00
Ten-dollar bills	70.00
Twenty-dollar bills	120.00
Total	$249.62

Page 67

	1	2	3	4	5	6	7	8	9
Pennies	$.01	$.02	$.03	$.04	$.05	$.06	$.07	$.08	$.09
Nickels	$.05	$.10	$.15	$.20	$.25	$.30	$.35	$.40	$.45
Dimes	$.10	$.20	$.30	$.40	$.50	$.60	$.70	$.80	$.90
Quarters	$.25	$.50	$.75	$1.00	$1.25	$1.50	$1.75	$2.00	$2.25
Half-dollars	$.50	$1.00	$1.50	$2.00	$2.50	$3.00	$3.50	$4.00	$4.50
One-dollar Bills	$1.00	$2.00	$3.00	$4.00	$5.00	$6.00	$7.00	$8.00	$9.00
Five-dollar Bills	$5.00	$10.00	$15.00	$20.00	$25.00	$30.00	$35.00	$40.00	$45.00
Ten-dollar Bills	$10.00	$20.00	$30.00	$40.00	$50.00	$60.00	$70.00	$80.00	$90.00
Twenty-dollar Bills	$20.00	$40.00	$60.00	$80.00	$100.00	$120.00	$140.00	$160.00	$180.00
Fifty-dollar Bills	$50.00	$100.00	$150.00	$200.00	$250.00	$300.00	$350.00	$400.00	$450.00

Pennies	$.09
Nickels	.45
Dimes	.90
Quarters	2.25
Half-dollars	4.50
One-dollar bills	9.00
Five-dollar bills	45.00
Ten-dollar bills	90.00
Twenty-dollar bills	180.00
Fifty-dollar bills	450.00
Total	$782.19

Page 68

A.
```
    $.35
     .70
    2.20
    3.00
    4.00
   24.00
   35.00
   30.00
+  40.00
$139.25
$284.72
```

B.
```
    $.72
     .60
     .90
    1.75
    2.50
    9.00
   20.00
   60.00
+  50.00
$145.47
```

Page 69

C.
```
    $.24
    1.25
    1.60
    5.50
    5.50
   18.00
   50.00
   30.00
   80.00
+ 125.00
$317.09
 $143.59
```

D.
```
   $3.16
   14.60
   38.70
   66.00
   98.50
+ 430.00
$650.96
```

Page 70

E.		F.	
$.98		$4.57	
.80		4.80	
1.30		8.40	
4.00		21.50	
5.00		15.50	
12.00		120.00	
50.00		510.00	
30.00		440.00	
+ 60.00		+ 37.00	
$164.08		$1,161.77	
$206.82			
$1.92			

Page 71

$1.06	$.23
.85	.60
2.50	1.90
2.00	2.50
3.00	4.50
28.00	35.00
65.00	90.00
+20.00	+60.00
$122.41	$194.73
$317.14	$72.32

Page 72

$.34	$.57
2.10	4.05
3.10	2.00
2.50	2.25
2.50	3.00
24.00	31.00
45.00	40.00
+10.00	+30.00
$89.54	$112.87
$202.41	$23.33

Page 73

	1	2	3	4	5	6	7	8	9
Pennies	$.01	$.02	$.03	$.04	$.05	$.06	$.07	$.08	$.09
Nickels	$.05	$.10	$.15	$.20	$.25	$.30	$.35	$.40	
Dimes	$.10	$.20	$.30	$.40	$.50	$.60	$.70		
Quarters	$.25	$.50	$.75	$1.00	$1.25	$1.50	$1.75	$2.00	
Half-dollars	$.50	$1.00	$1.50	$2.00	$2.50	$3.00	$3.50		
One-dollar Bills	$1.00	$2.00	$3.00	$4.00	$5.00	$6.00			
Five-dollar Bills	$5.00	$10.00	$15.00	$20.00	$25.00	$30.00	$35.00		
Ten-dollar Bills	$10.00	$20.00	$30.00	$40.00	$50.00	$60.00			
Twenty-dollar Bills	$20.00	$40.00	$60.00	$80.00	$100.00				
Fifty-dollar Bills	$50.00	$100.00	$150.00						

Pennies	$.09
Nickels	.40
Dimes	.70
Quarters	2.00
Half-dollars	3.50
One-dollar bills	6.00
Five-dollar bills	35.00
Ten-dollar bills	60.00
Twenty-dollar bills	100.00
Fifty-dollar bills	150.00
Total	$357.69
	$35.92

Page 74

$1.16	$.35
.65	.85
.30	2.30
2.25	1.75
3.50	2.50
17.00	26.00
60.00	80.00
+40.00	+50.00
$124.86	$163.75
$288.61	$38.89

Page 75

1. $12.97
2. $109.00
3. $175.50
4. $113.99

Page 76

1.	$59.00	6.	$380.00
2.	$17.82	7.	$137.26
3.	$56.71	8.	$866.90
4.	$76.39	9.	$84.88
5.	$93.57	10.	$552.71

Page 77

1.	$12.02	6.	$187.00
2.	$16.00	7.	$184.63
3.	$7.12	8.	$482.75
4.	$51.57	9.	$88.36
5.	$45.55	10.	$81.25

Page 78

1.	$24.26	6.	$84.00
2.	$27.00	7.	$1,160.00
3.	$25.22	8.	$88.50
4.	$30.28	9.	$91.92
5.	$64.32	10.	$658.41

USING MONEY

Page 79
1. $139.52
2. $22.12
3. $81.43
4. $75.04
5. $222.62
6. $176.58
7. $834.64
8. $51.25
9. $123.50
10. $467.48

Page 80
1. $18.58
2. $159.36
3. $38.12
4. $184.96
5. $67.93
6. $924.42
7. $366.41
8. $1,256.57
9. $129.21
10. $1,816.82

Page 81
1. $3.40
2. $7.92
3. $6.87
4. $7.95
5. $15.52
6. $15.98
7. $29.94
8. $22.00
9. $39.96
10. $17.91
11. $24.95
12. $109.90

Page 82
1. $3.16
2. $4.40
3. $5.31
4. $7.45
5. $19.52
6. $17.90
7. $29.97
8. $31.00
9. $37.90
10. $14.32
11. $79.76
12. $39.95

Page 83
1.	$29.35	$52.83	$117.40
2.	$41.25	$68.75	$192.50
3.	$19.00	$33.25	$57.00
4.	$45.00	$90.00	$180.00
5.	$77.94		

6. $13.50
7. $10.76
8. $1,016.00
9. $3,375.00
10. $63.75

Page 84
1.	$45.00	$150.00	$262.50
2.	$63.00	$110.25	$236.25
3.	$8.85	$14.75	$29.50
4.	$9.00		
5.	$7.96		
6.	$99.40		
7.	$270.00		
8.	$450.00		
9.	$62.02		
10.	$8.75		

Page 85
1. $4.50
2. $8.97
3. $17.50
4. $34.65
5. $52.48
6. $38.45
7. $34.75
8. $2.46
9. $.73
10. $29.00

Page 86
1. $4.60
2. $8.97
3. $17.50
4. $72.45
5. $44.90
6. $16.75
7. $29.85
8. $111.50
9. $35.50
10. $23.98

Page 87
1.	$42.80	$162.64	$256.80
2.	$50.25	$117.25	$268.00
3.	$122.25		
4.	$11.75		
5.	$722.75		
6.	$144.75		
7.	$47.50		
8.	$34.95		
9.	$11.25		
10.	$47.25		

Page 88
1. $9.88
2. $23.95
3. $162.50

4. $48.67
5. $59.94
6. $45.60
7.	$64.12	$183.20	$329.76
8.	$72.50	$116.00	$217.50
9.	$40.46	$115.60	$208.08
10.	$82.25	$235.00	$423.00

Page 89
1. $49.67
2. $72.09
3. $82.46
4. $4.49
5. $10.85
6. $279.89
7. $8.00
8. $6.59
9. $3.99
10. $12.93

Page 90
1. $884.46, $87.97

$$\begin{array}{r} \$490.50 \\ 93.18 \\ 105.28 \\ +195.50 \\ \hline \$884.46 \end{array} \qquad \begin{array}{r} \$972.43 \\ -884.46 \\ \hline \$87.97 \end{array}$$

2. $10.54
3. $7.02
4. $37.78
5. $191.00
6. $8.775 = $8.78
7. $7.64
8. $54.50

Page 91
1. $374.86
2. $12.37
3. $25.85
4. $101.54
5. $8.92
6. $178.55
7. $539.77
8 $23.50
9.	$48.64	$42.56	$182.40
10.	$66.25	$119.25	$159.00
11.	$82.50	$115.50	$198.00
12.	$34.68	$46.24	$173.40

Page 92
1. $110.57
2. $11.61
3. $109.25
4. $20.25
5. $39.50
6. $14.0625 = $14.07

7. $12.67
8. $139.60
9. $27.40
10. $3,529.14
11. $18.72 $28.08 $187.20
12. $47.25 $126.00 $189.00

Page 93
1. $1,135.38, $68.14

```
   $715.50        $1,203.52
    121.28       - 1,135.38
    110.68            $68.14
  +187.92
 $1,135.38
```

2. $12.92
3. $214.10
4. $7.25
5. $177.85
6. $47.60
7. $238.25
8. $38.50

Page 94
1. $116.65
2. $68.93
3. $47.65
4. $177.85
5. $39.50
6. $345.50
7. $4.75
8. $1,004.42, $30.18

```
   $635.50        $1,034.60
     93.29       - 1,004.42
    130.25            $30.18
  +145.38
 $1,004.42
```

Page 95
1. $11.09
2. $635.92
3. $112.73
4. $177.35
5. $52.75
6. $21.35
7. $113.00
8. $12.75
9. $44.60
10. $27.50
11. $59.00 $103.25 $221.25
12. $10.60 $13.25 $39.75

Page 96
1. $135.50
2. $62.50
3. $23.95
4. $13.28
5. $88.93
6. $20.50
7. $126.24
8. $637.04
9. $804.05
10. $981.62, $102.91

```
   $650.00        $1,084.53
     98.13        - 981.62
     81.29            $102.91
  +152.20
  $981.62
```

Answer Key
Life Skills Mathematics

Basic Math

Consumer Math

Learning to Budget

Practical Math

Using Fractions

Using Money

AGS®

American Guidance Service, Inc.
4201 Woodland Road
Circle Pines, MN 55014-1796
1-800-328-2560

9 780785 409588

Product Number
ISBN 0-7854-

T3-CCK-754

AGS

Answer Key

Basic Math

Consumer Math

Learning to Budget

Practical Math

Using Fractions

Using Money

Life Skills Mathematics

Contents

Printed in the United States of America

ISBN 0–7854–0958–0

Product Number 90866

A 0 9 8 7 6 5 4 5 3